Non-Verbal Reasoning

The 11+
10-Minute Tests

For the CEM (Durham University) test

Ages
8-9

Practise • Prepare • Pass
Everything your child needs for 11+ success

How to use this book

This book is made up of 10-minute tests and puzzle pages.
There are answers and detailed explanations in the pull-out section at the back of the book.

10-Minute Tests

- There are 31 tests in this book, each containing 16 questions.

- Each test is designed to cover a good range of the question styles and topics that your child could come across in the non-verbal reasoning sections of their 11+ test.

- Your child should aim to score at least 14 in each 10-minute test.
  If they score less than this, use their results to work out the areas they need more practice on.

- If your child hasn't managed to finish the test in time, they need to work on increasing their speed, whereas if they have made a lot of mistakes, they need to work more carefully.

- Keep track of your child's scores using the progress chart on the inside back cover of the book.

Puzzle Pages

- There are 10 puzzle pages in this book, which are a great break from test-style questions.
  They encourage children to practise the same skills that they will need in the test, but in a fun way.

Published by CGP

Editors:
Marc Barnard, Alex Fairer, Katherine Faudemer.

With thanks to Amanda MacNaughton and Jack Perry for the proofreading.

Please note that CGP is not associated with CEM or The University of Durham in any way.
This book does not include any official questions and it is not endorsed by CEM or The University of Durham.
CEM, Centre for Evaluation and Monitoring, Durham University and *The University of Durham*
are all trademarks of The University of Durham.

ISBN: 978 1 78294 775 2
Printed by Elanders Ltd, Newcastle upon Tyne
Clipart from Corel®

Based on the classic CGP style created by Richard Parsons.

Text, design, layout and original illustrations © Coordination Group Publications Ltd. (CGP) 2017
All rights reserved.

Contents

Question Type Examples

These pages contain a completed example question for each question type that appears in this book. Have a look through them to familiarise yourself with the question types before you do the tests.

Odd One Out

Find the figure in each row that is most unlike the other figures.

Example:

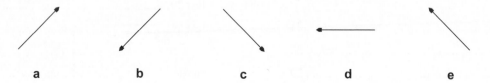

    a   b   c   d   e

Answer: d

In all other figures, the arrow points diagonally.

Find the Figure Like the First Two

Work out which option is most like the two figures on the left.

Example:

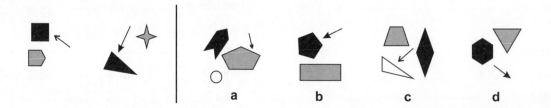

                       a   b   c   d

Answer: b

All figures must have an arrow pointing at a black shape.

Find the Figure Like the First Three

Work out which option is most like the three figures on the left.

Example:

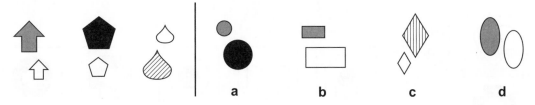

a   b   c   d

Answer: c

All figures must have a large grey, black or hatched shape and a smaller white version of that shape.

Complete the Pair

Look at how the first figure is changed, and then work out which option would look like the second figure if you changed it in the same way.

Example:

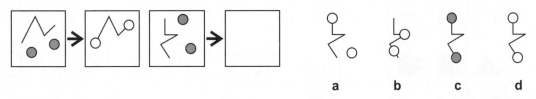

a   b   c   d

Answer: d

The two circles move to the ends of the line and turn white.

Work out which of the options best fits in place of the missing square in the grid.

Example:

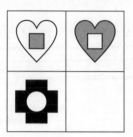

a   b   c   d   e

Answer: a

Working from left to right, the two shapes swap shadings.

Work out which of the options best fits in place of the missing square in the grid.

Example:

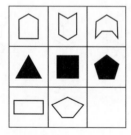

a   b   c   d   e

Answer: c

Working from left to right, the number of sides of the shape increases by one in each grid square.

     4

Complete the Series

Work out which of the options best fits in place of the missing square in the series.

Example:

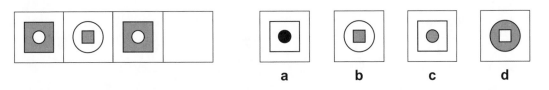

a   b   c   d

Answer: b

The figures alternate between a white circle in a grey square and a grey square in a white circle.

Work out which of the options best fits in place of the missing square in the series.

Example:

a   b   c   d

Answer: c

In each series square, the black shading moves one rectangle to the right.

5

Rotate the Figure

Work out which option would look like the figure on the left if it was rotated.

Example:

 Rotate

| a | b | c | d |

Answer: d

The figure has been rotated 90 degrees clockwise.

Reflect the Figure

Work out which option would look like the figure on the left if it was reflected over the line.

Example:

Reflect

| a | b | c | d |

Answer: b

Options A and D are rotations of the shape on the left. Option C has not been reflected.

Look at the Figure from the Top

Work out which option is a top-down 2D view of the 3D figure on the left.

Example:

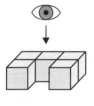

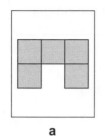

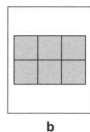

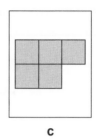

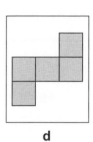

a   b   c   d

Answer: a

There are five cubes visible from above.
There should be two cubes on the right of the figure and two at the front of the figure.

Look at the Figure from the Right

Work out which option is the 3D figure viewed from the right.

Example:

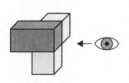

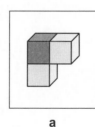

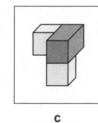

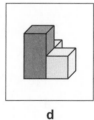

a   b   c   d

Answer: b

There should be a block two cubes long on the left of the figure at the top.
There should be a cube on the right of the figure and a cube at the bottom.

You have **10 minutes** to do this test. Circle the letter for each correct answer.

Find the figure in each row that is most unlike the others.

1.

  a   b   c   d   e

2.

  a   b   c   d   e

3.

  a   b   c   d   e

4.

  a   b   c   d   e

8

Work out which option would look like the figure on the left if it was rotated.

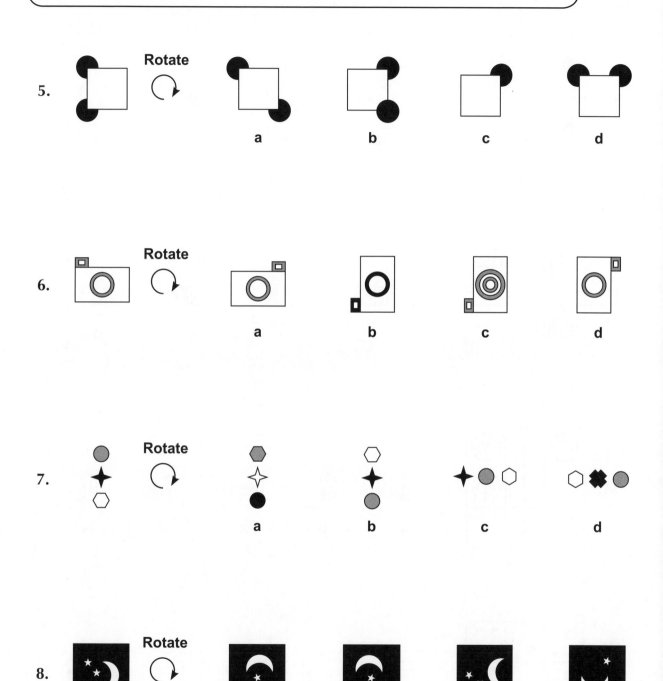

5.

Rotate

a   b   c   d

6.

Rotate

a   b   c   d

7.

Rotate

a   b   c   d

8.

Rotate

a   b   c   d

Test 1

Work out which of the options best fits in place of the missing square in the grid.

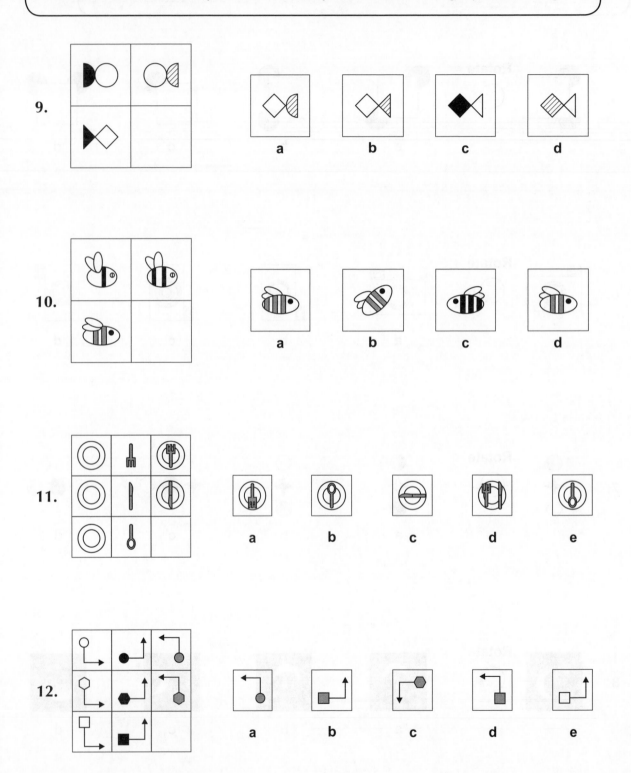

9.

a   b   c   d

10.

a   b   c   d

11.

a   b   c   d   e

12.

a   b   c   d   e

Work out which option is a top-down 2D view of the 3D figure on the left.

13.

a   b   c   d

14.

a   b   c   d

15.

a   b   c   d

16.

a   b   c   d

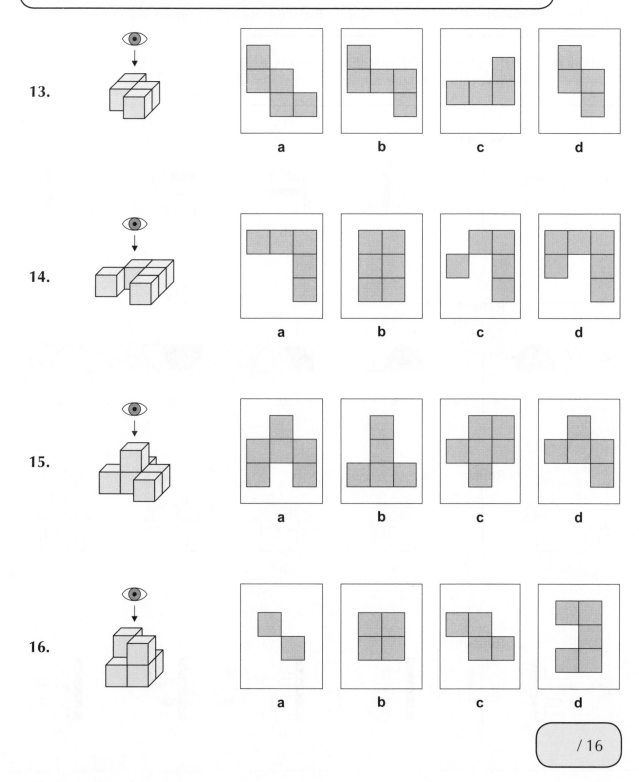

/ 16

11

Test 2

You have **10 minutes** to do this test. Circle the letter for each correct answer.

> Work out which option would look like the figure on the left if it was reflected over the line.

Reflect

1.

                  a   b   c   d

Reflect

2.

                  a   b   c   d

Reflect

3.

                  a   b   c   d

Reflect

4.

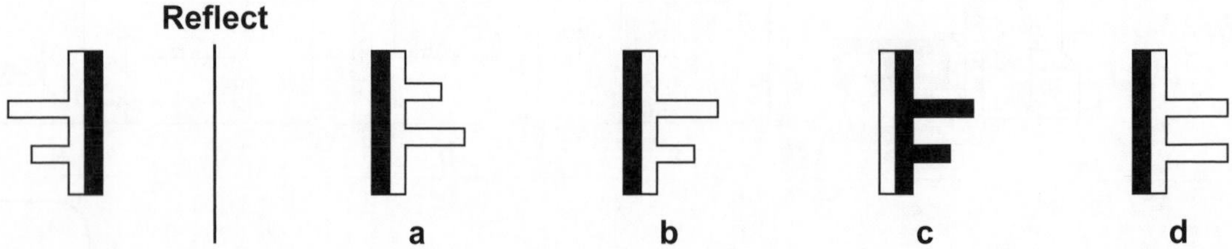

                  a   b   c   d

Work out which option is most like the two figures on the left.

5.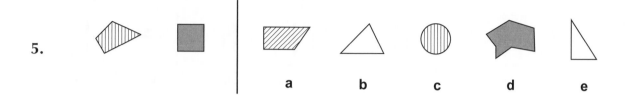

a   b   c   d   e

6.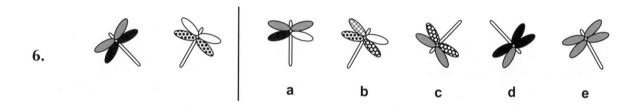

a   b   c   d   e

7.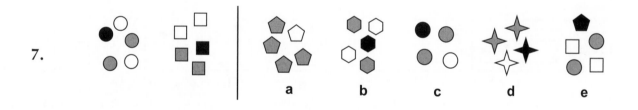

a   b   c   d   e

8.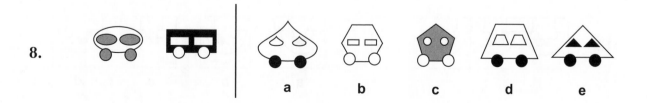

a   b   c   d   e

Test 2

Work out which of the options best fits in place of the missing square in the series.

9.

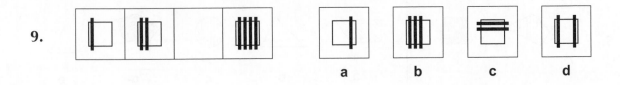

a   b   c   d

10.

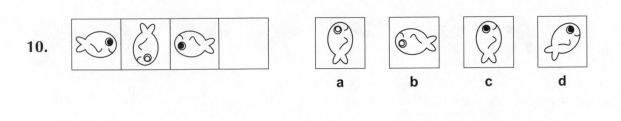

a   b   c   d

11.

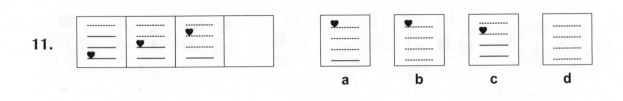

a   b   c   d

12.

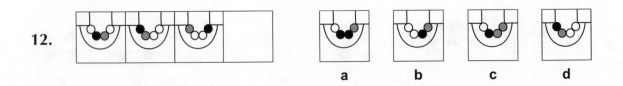

a   b   c   d

Work out which option is the 3D figure viewed from the **right**.

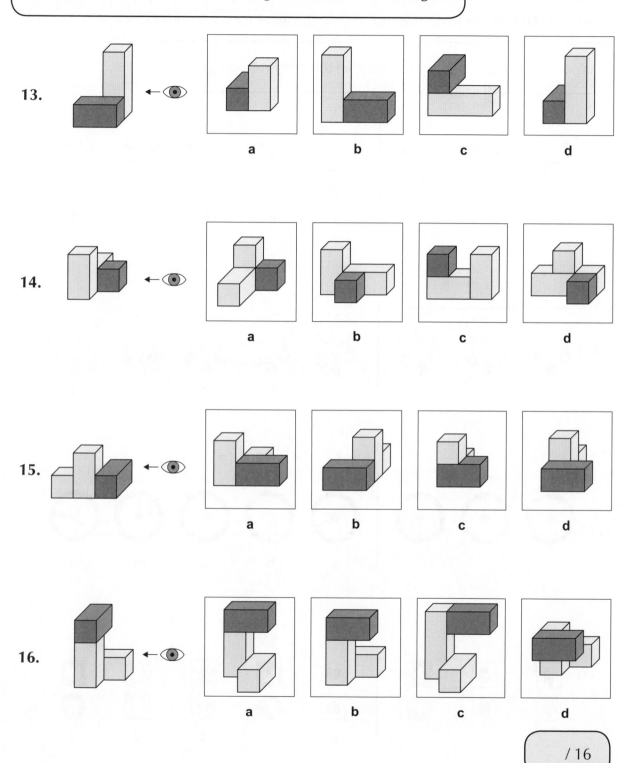

13.

14.

15.

16.

/ 16

15

Test 3

You have **10 minutes** to do this test. Circle the letter for each correct answer.

Work out which option is most like the three figures on the left.

1.
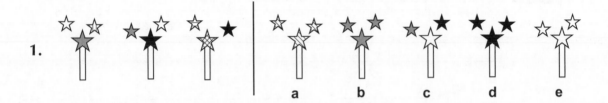

2.
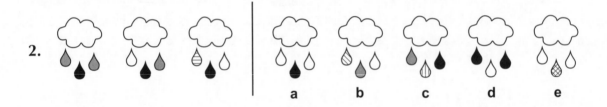

3.
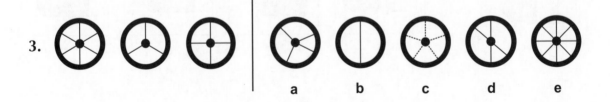

4.

Work out which option would look like the figure on the left if it was reflected over the line.

Reflect

5. |

                 a   b   c   d

Reflect

6. |

                 a   b   c   d

Reflect

7. |

                 a   b   c   d

Reflect

8. | 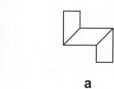

                 a   b   c   d

17

Work out which of the options best fits in place of the missing square in the grid.

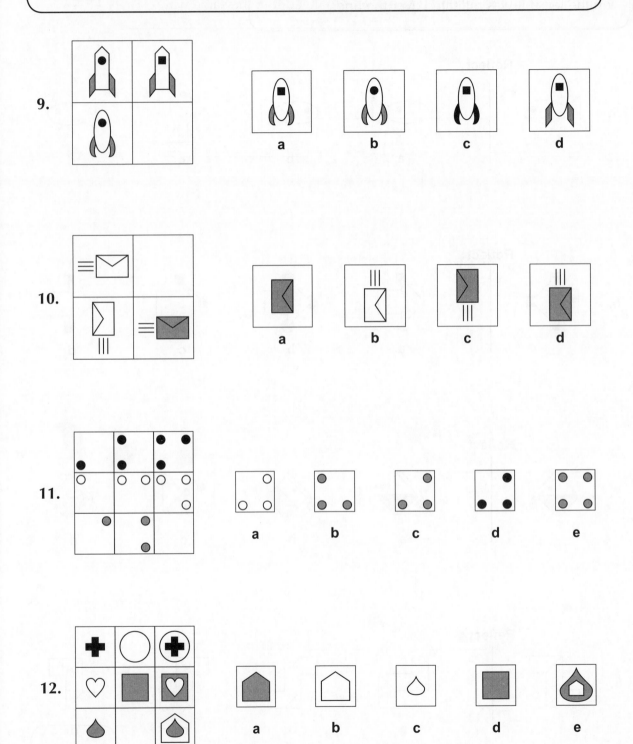

9.

a   b   c   d

10.

a   b   c   d

11.

a   b   c   d   e

12.

a   b   c   d   e

18

Look at how the first figure is changed, and then work out which option would look like the second figure if you changed it in the same way.

13.

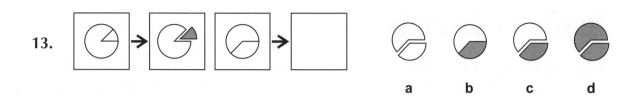

a   b   c   d

14.

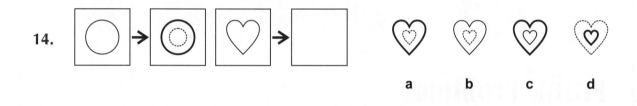

a   b   c   d

15.

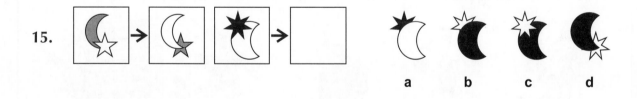

a   b   c   d

16.

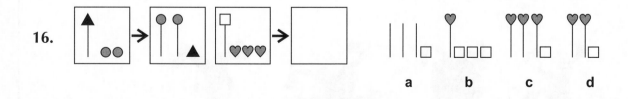

a   b   c   d

/ 16

19

Puzzles 1

These puzzles are a great way to practise **spotting similarities** and **reflections**.

Feathery Friends

Penelope Penguin and Doris Duck are very fashionable. They want an owl with similar style to be friends with. Circle the owl that best shares their style.

  A   B   C   D

Prank Problems

Tom is waiting behind a wall with a water balloon to throw at his Dad. All he can see are people's shadows as they pass by and he doesn't want to hit the wrong person. Match the people to their shadows below.

Tom's Dad   Tom's PE   Tom's maths   Tom's scout
               teacher   teacher   leader

  A   B   C   D

Test 4

You have **10 minutes** to do this test. Circle the letter for each correct answer.

Work out which option is most like the two figures on the left.

1.

  a   b   c   d   e

2.

  a   b   c   d   e

3.

  a   b   c   d   e

4.

  a   b   c   d   e

21

Work out which option is a top-down 2D view of the 3D figure on the left.

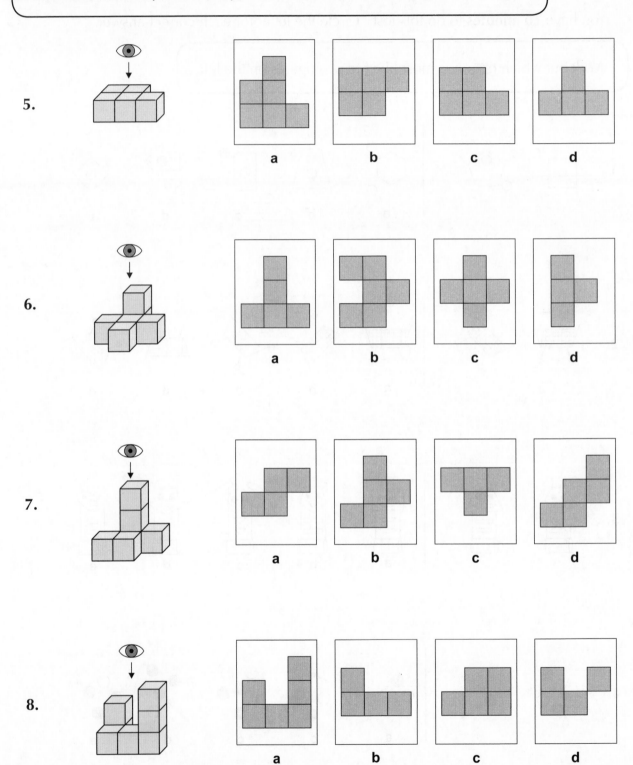

5.

a   b   c   d

6.

a   b   c   d

7.

a   b   c   d

8.

a   b   c   d

Work out which option would look like the figure on the left if it was rotated.

9. **Rotate**

                                         a   b   c   d

10. **Rotate**   a   b   d

11. **Rotate**   a

12. **Rotate**   a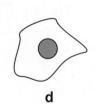

Work out which of the options best fits in place of the missing square in the series.

13.

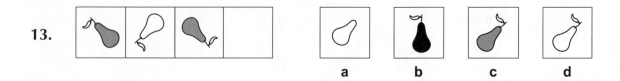

       a   b   c   d

14.

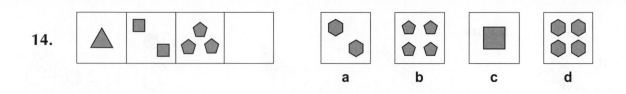

       a   b   c   d

15.

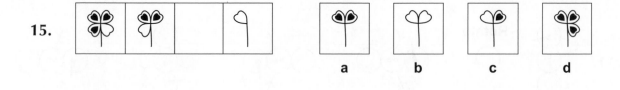

       a   b   c   d

16.

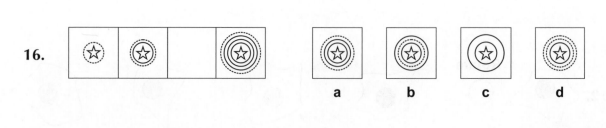

       a   b   c   d

/ 16

You have **10 minutes** to do this test. Circle the letter for each correct answer.

Work out which option is the 3D figure viewed from the **right**.

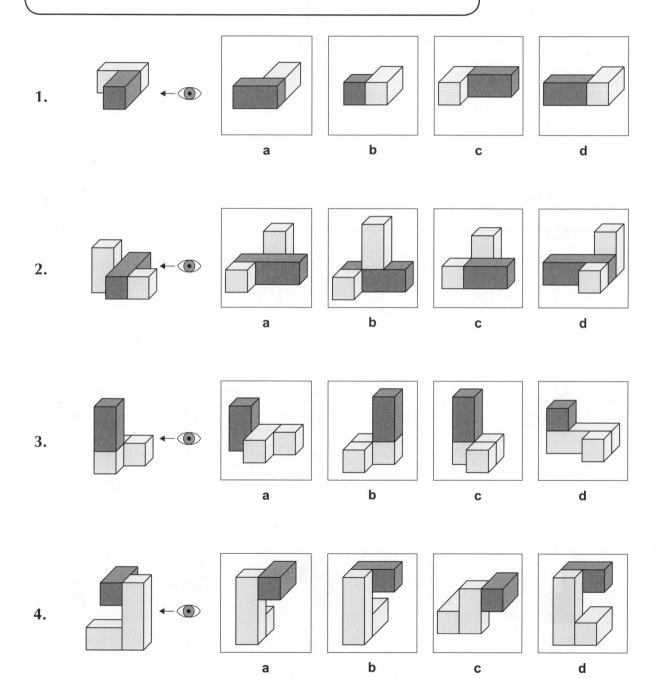

1.
a b c d

2.
a b c d

3.
a b c d

4.
a b c d

Test 5

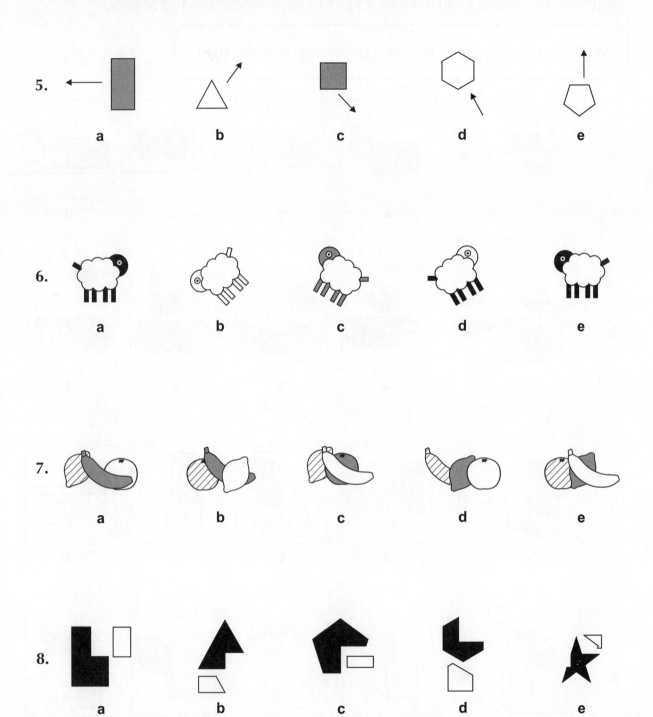

5. a b c d e

6. a b c d e

7. a b c d e

8. a b c d e

Work out which option would look like the figure on the left if it was reflected over the line.

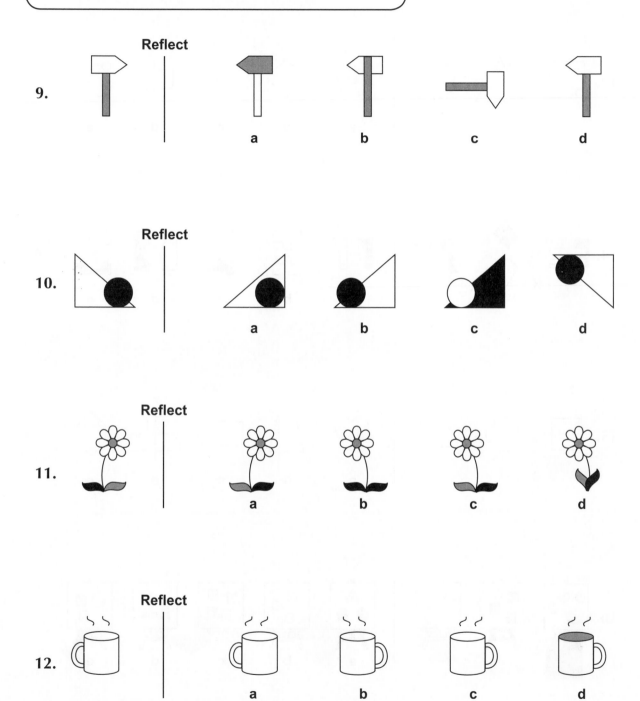

9.

Reflect

a   b   c   d

10.

Reflect

a   b   c   d

11.

Reflect

a   b   c   d

12.

Reflect

a   b   c   d

27

Work out which option is most like the three figures on the left.

13.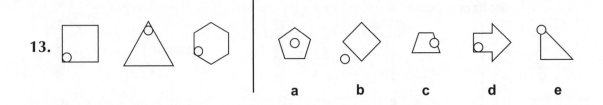

a   b   c   d   e

14.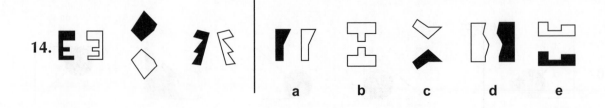

a   b   c   d   e

15.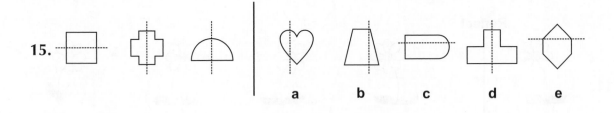

a   b   c   d   e

16.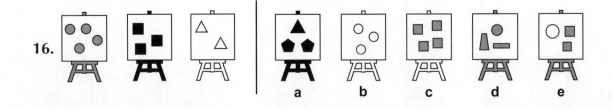

a   b   c   d   e

/ 16

You have **10 minutes** to do this test. Circle the letter for each correct answer.

> Work out which option would look like the figure on the left if it was rotated.

1. 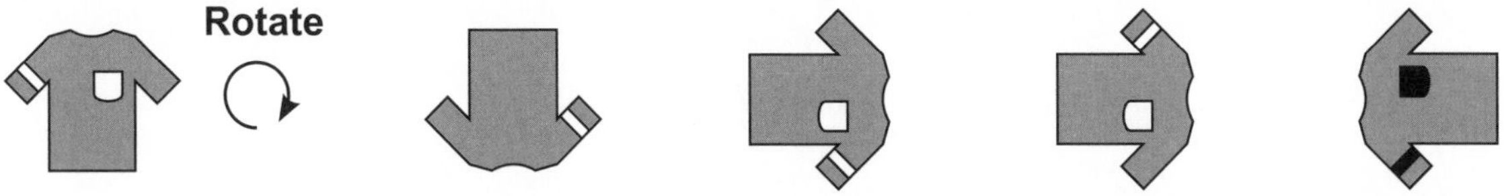 **Rotate**

                                            a   **b**   **c**   **d**

2. **Rotate**

                                            a   **b**   **c**   **d**

3. **Rotate**

                                            a   **b**   **c**   **d**

4.  **Rotate**

                                            a   **b**   **c**   **d**

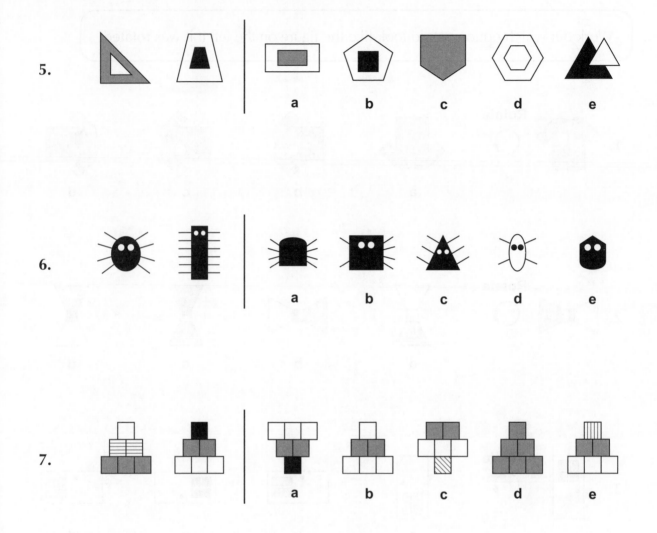

5.

a   b   c   d   e

6.

a   b   c   d   e

7.

a   b   c   d   e

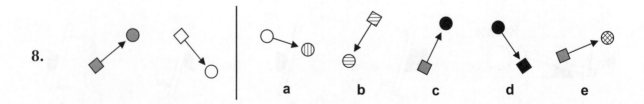

8.

a   b   c   d   e

Work out which of the options best fits in place of the missing square in the grid.

9.

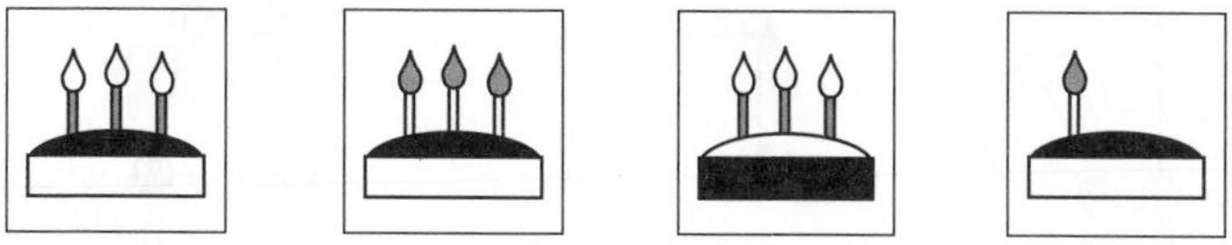

a   b   c   d

10.

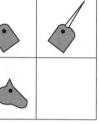

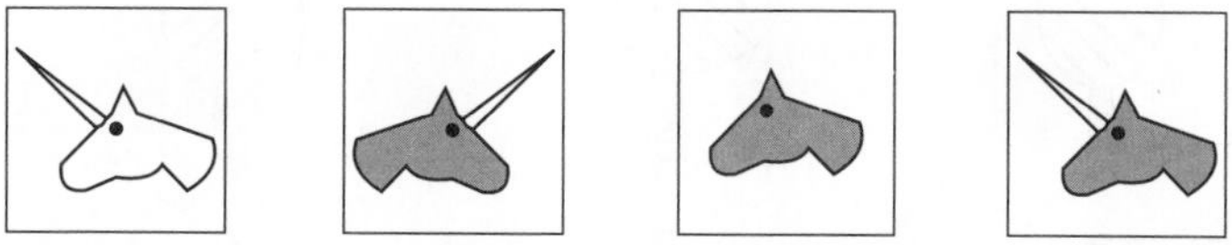

a   b   c   d

11.

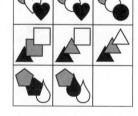

a   b   c   d   e

12.

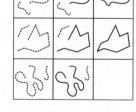

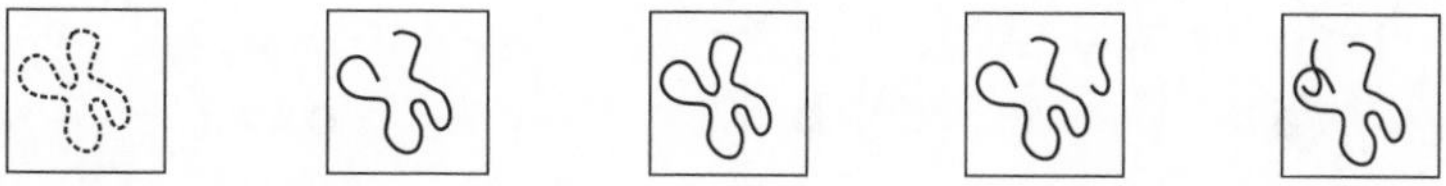

a   b   c   d   e

Test 6

Find the figure in each row that is most unlike the others.

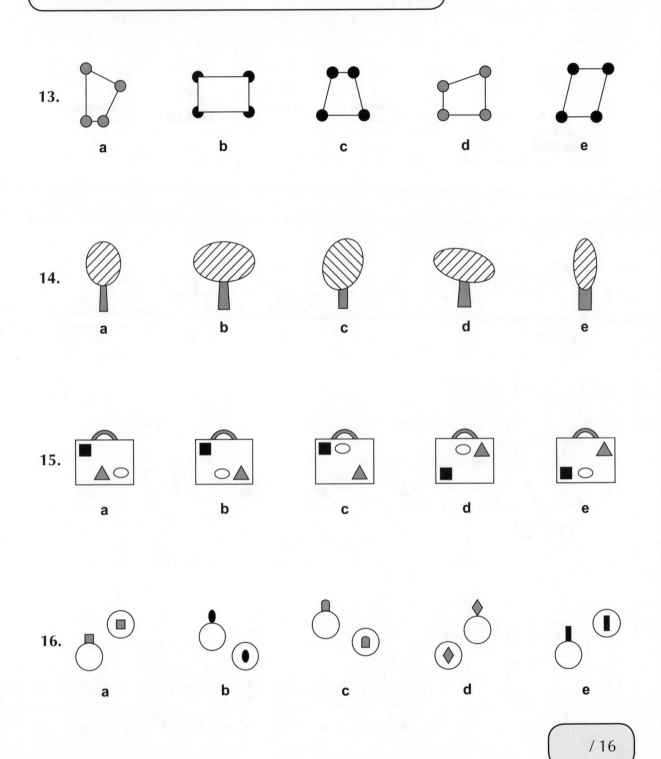

13.
a   b   c   d   e

14.
a   b   c   d   e

15.
a   b   c   d   e

16.
a   b   c   d   e

/ 16

Puzzles 2

Have a go at these puzzles to practise **comparing things** and **rotating shapes**.

Clive's Jewellery Shop

Clive has a jewellery shop. He likes to put all of the similar necklaces in one place. He puts the three necklaces below together.
Draw another necklace that Clive could put with these three necklaces.

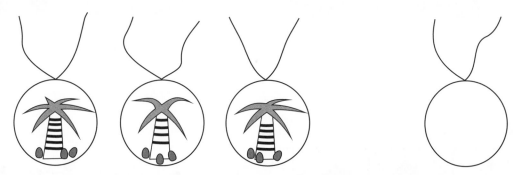

Lilypad Hop

Freddy needs to hop back to the river bank using the lilypads below.
However, some of the lilypads sink.
Lilypads that are safe to hop on are marked with this symbol:
The symbol **can be rotated**.
Find Freddy a safe path back to the river bank.

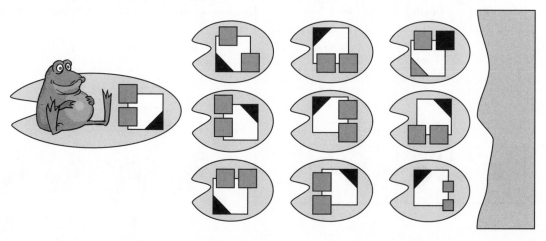

33

Test 7

You have **10 minutes** to do this test. Circle the letter for each correct answer.

Look at how the first figure is changed, and then work out which option would look like the second figure if you changed it in the same way.

1.

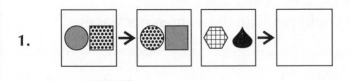

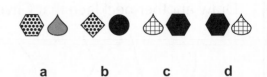

               a   b   c   d

2.

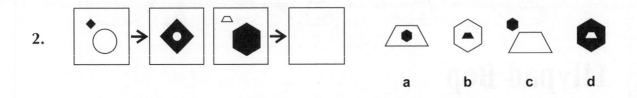

               a   b   c   d

3.

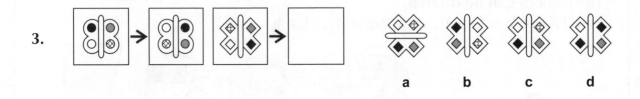

               a   b   c   d

4.

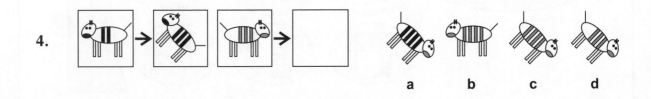

               a   b   c   d

    34

Work out which option would look like the figure on the left if it was reflected over the line.

Reflect

5.

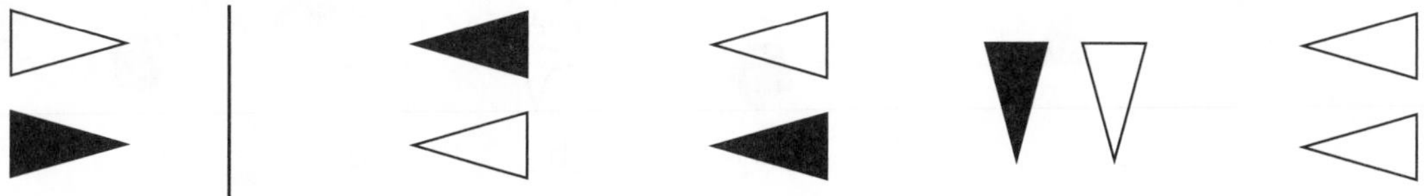

a   b   c   d

Reflect

6.

a   b   c   d

Reflect

7.

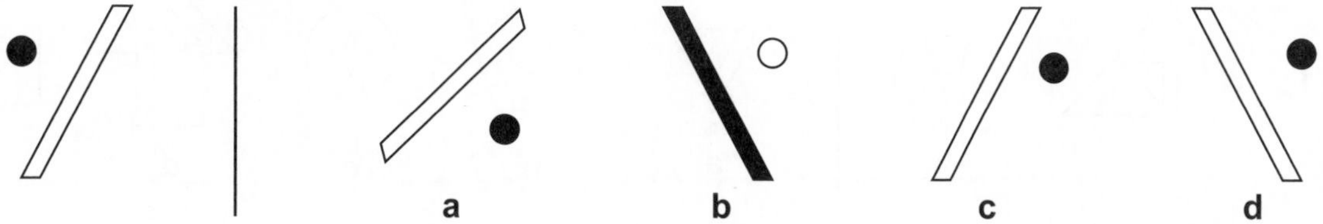

a   b   c   d

Reflect

8.

a   b   c   d

Work out which option is most like the two figures on the left.

9.

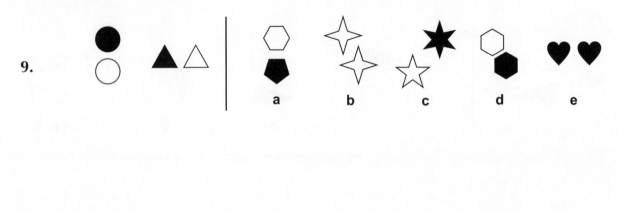

a   b   c   d   e

10.

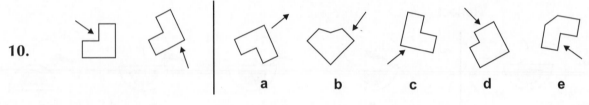

a   b   c   d   e

11.

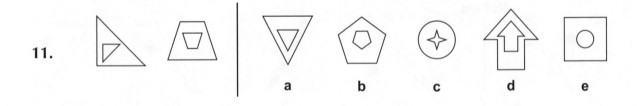

a   b   c   d   e

12.

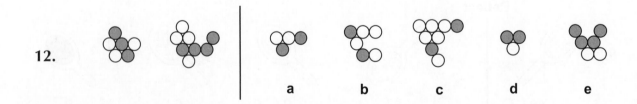

a   b   c   d   e

Work out which option is a top-down 2D view of the 3D figure on the left.

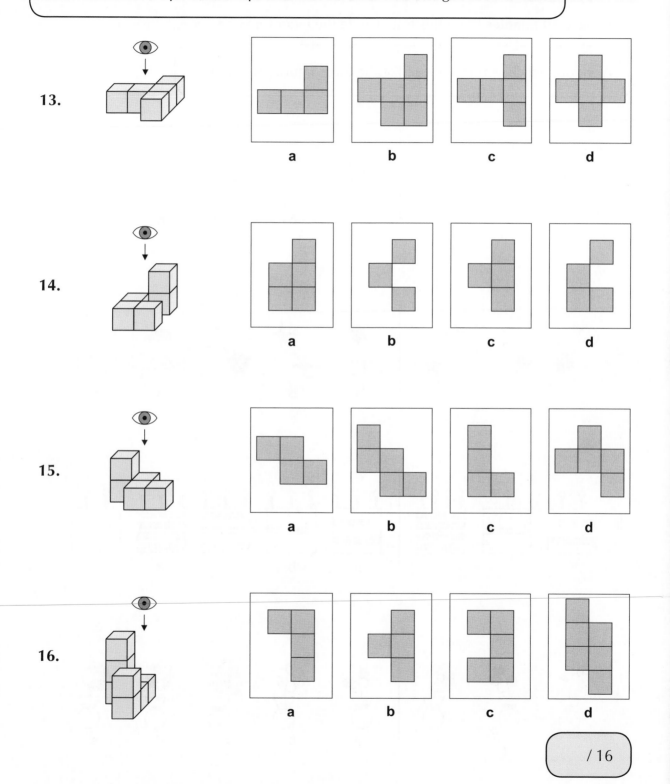

13.

a   b   c   d

14.

a   b   c   d

15.

a   b   c   d

16.

a   b   c   d

/ 16

37

Test 8

You have **10 minutes** to do this test. Circle the letter for each correct answer.

> Work out which option is most like the three figures on the left.

1.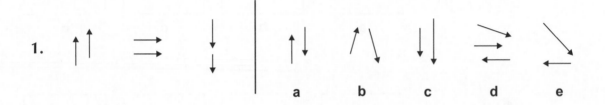

                                     a   b   c   d   e

2.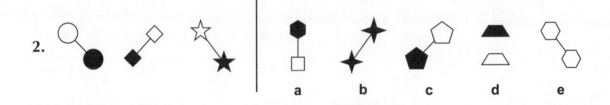

                                     a   b   c   d   e

3.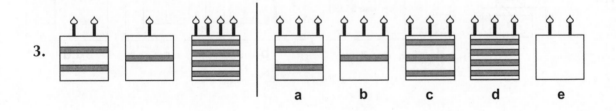

                                     a   b   c   d   e

4.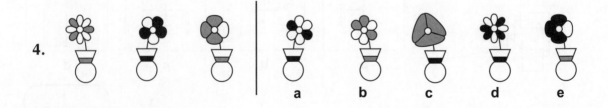

                                     a   b   c   d   e

Work out which of the options best fits in place of the missing square in the series.

5.

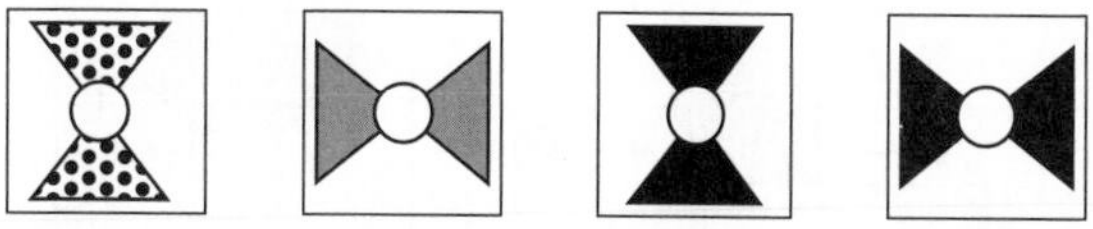

a   b   c   d

6.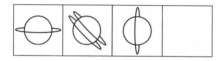

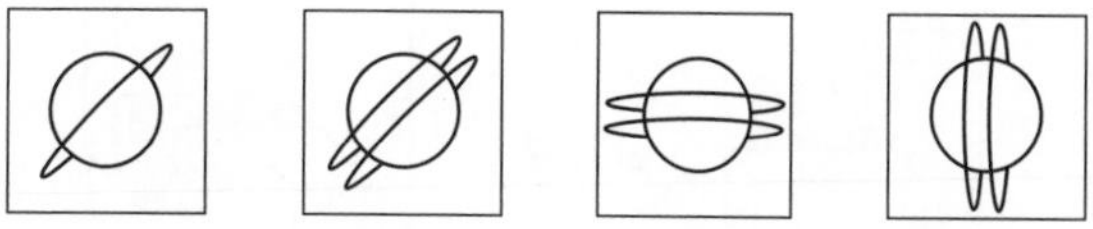

a   b   c   d

7.

a   b   c   d

8.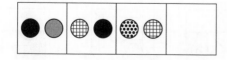

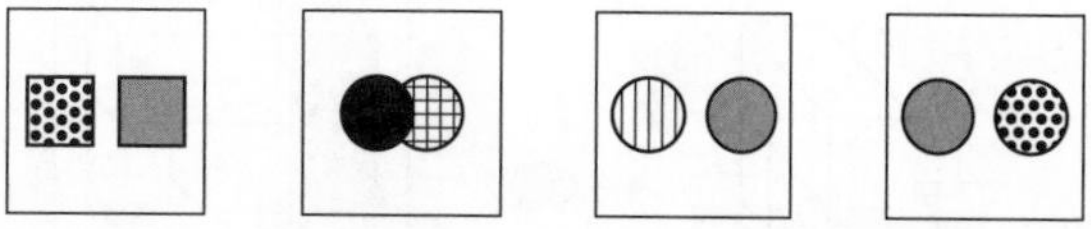

a   b   c   d

39

Work out which option is the 3D figure viewed from the **right**.

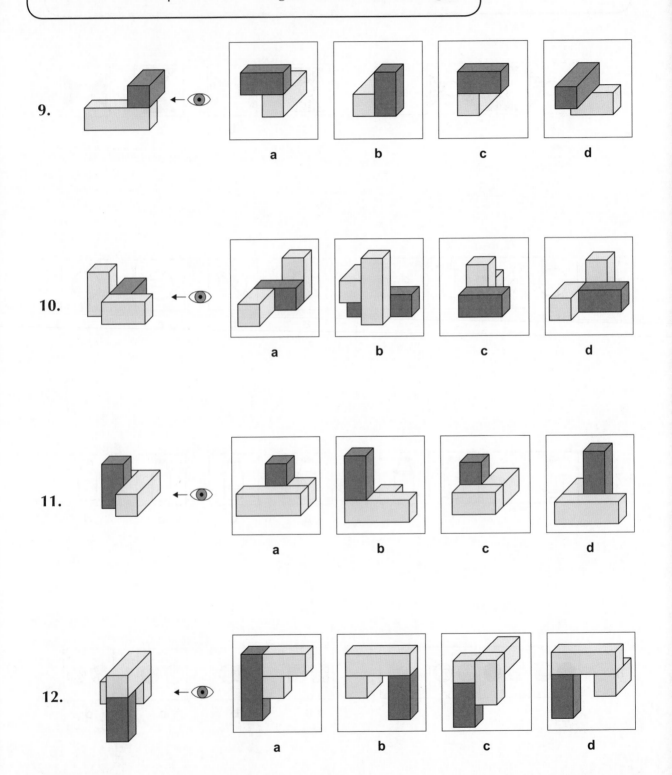

9.

a

b

c

d

10.

a

b

c

d

11.

a

b

c

d

12.

a

b

c

d

40

Work out which option would look like the figure on the left if it was rotated.

13. **Rotate** ↻

a   b   c   d

14. **Rotate** ↻

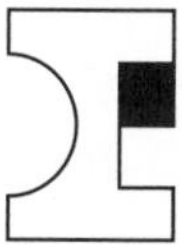

a   b   c   d

15. **Rotate** ↻

a   b   c   d

16. **Rotate** ↻

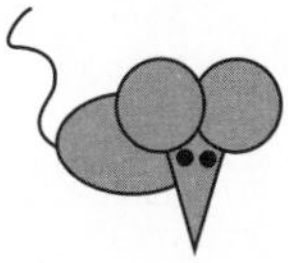

a   b   c   d

/ 16

41

Test 8

You have **10 minutes** to do this test. Circle the letter for each correct answer.

Work out which of the options best fits in place of the missing square in the grid.

1.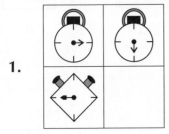

a   b   c   d   e

2.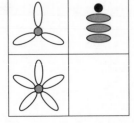

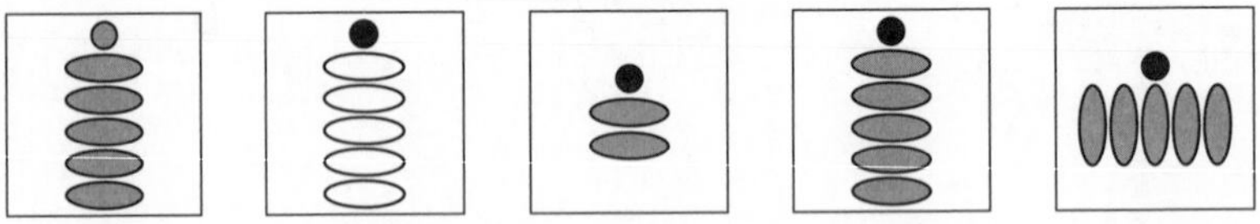

a   b   c   d   e

3.

a   b   c   d   e

4.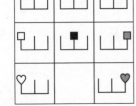

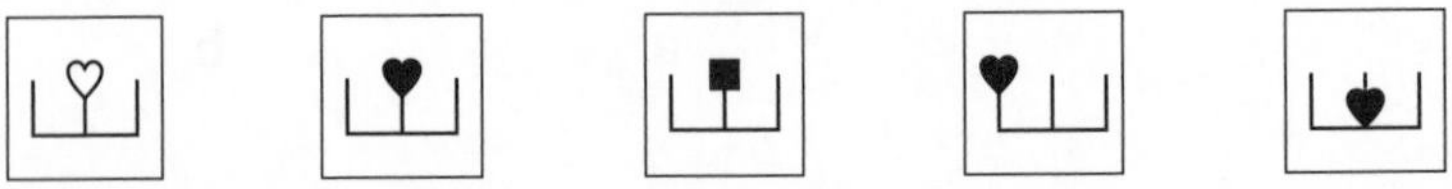

a   b   c   d   e

Find the figure in each row that is most unlike the others.

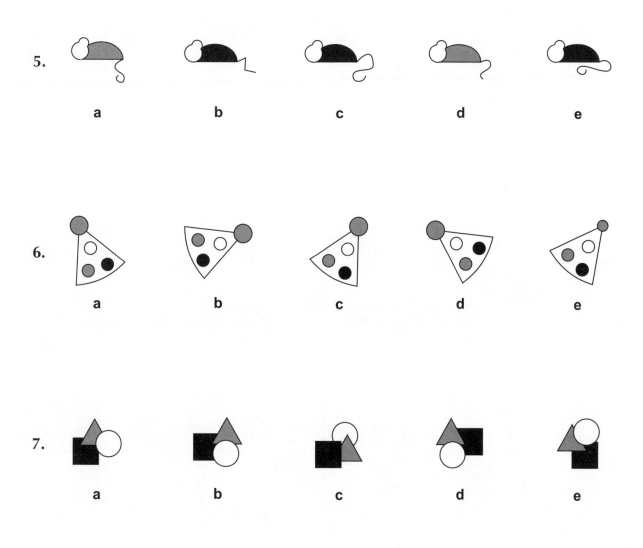

5.

a   b   c   d   e

6.

a   b   c   d   e

7.

a   b   c   d   e

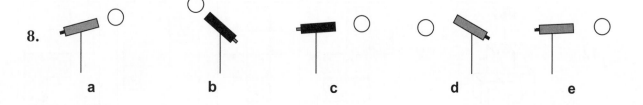

8.

a   b   c   d   e

Test 9

Work out which option is a top-down 2D view of the 3D figure on the left.

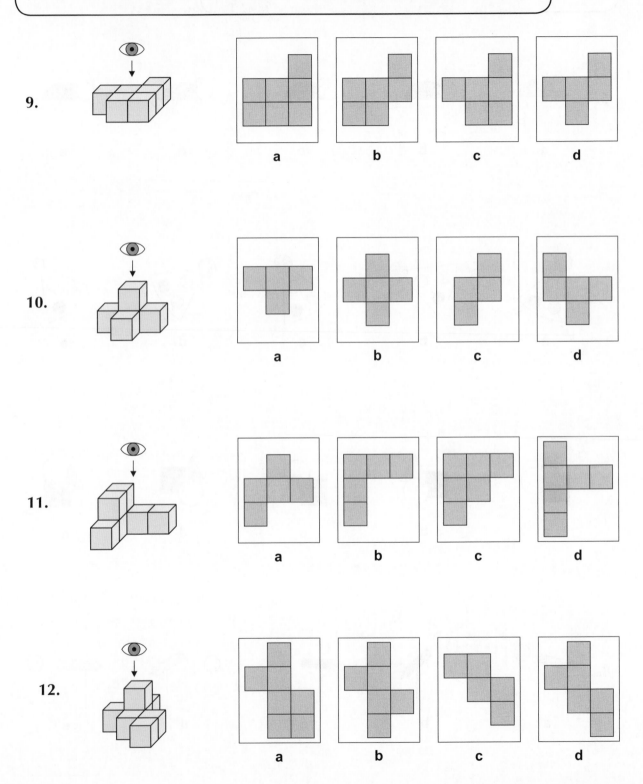

9.

    a   b   c   d

10.

    a   b   c   d

11.

    a   b   c   d

12.

    a   b   c   d

Look at how the first figure is changed, and then work out which option would look like the second figure if you changed it in the same way.

13.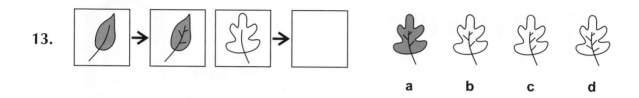

                a   b   c   d

14.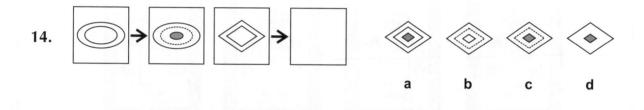

                a   b   c   d

15.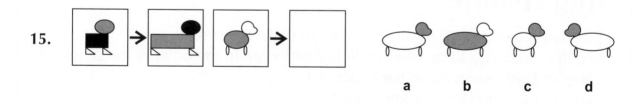

                a   b   c   d

16.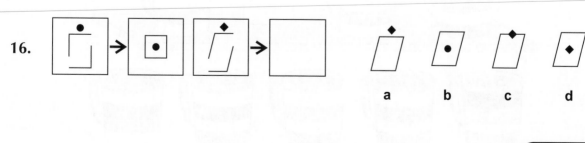

                a   b   c   d

/ 16

45

It's time for some more puzzles — this time to practise spotting **reflections** and **patterns**.

Robot Reflections

Robert the Robot is looking in the mirror.
Which mirror shows Robert's reflection?

     A   **B**   **C**   **D**

Mug Muddle

Faye has four mugs. The patterns on them make a series.
She likes the mugs to be lined up in her cupboard in the order of the series.
Three of Faye's mugs are in her cupboard.
Which mug (A-E) is Faye's other mug?

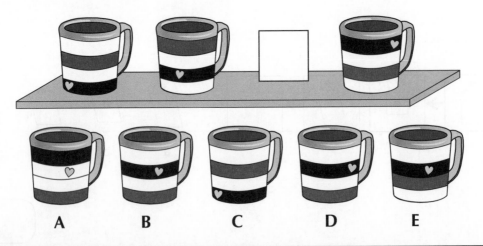

   A   **B**   **C**   **D**   **E**

Test 10

You have **10 minutes** to do this test. Circle the letter for each correct answer.

Work out which of the options best fits in place of the missing square in the series.

1.

                                                      a   b   c   d

2.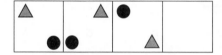

3.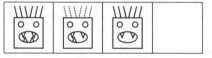

4.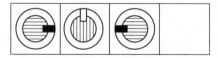

Work out which option is most like the three figures on the left.

5.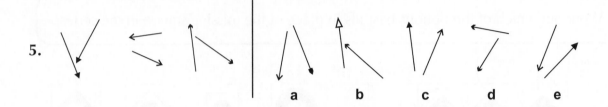

                            a   b   c   d   e

6.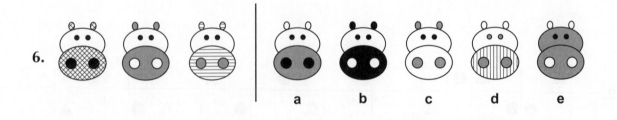

                            a   b   c   d   e

7.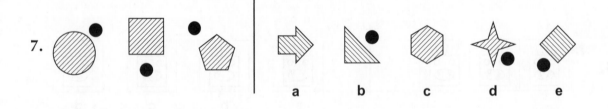

                            a   b   c   d   e

8.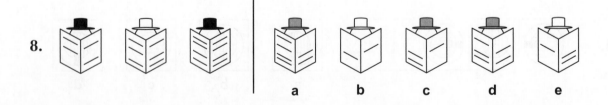

                            a   b   c   d   e

Work out which option is the 3D figure viewed from the **right**.

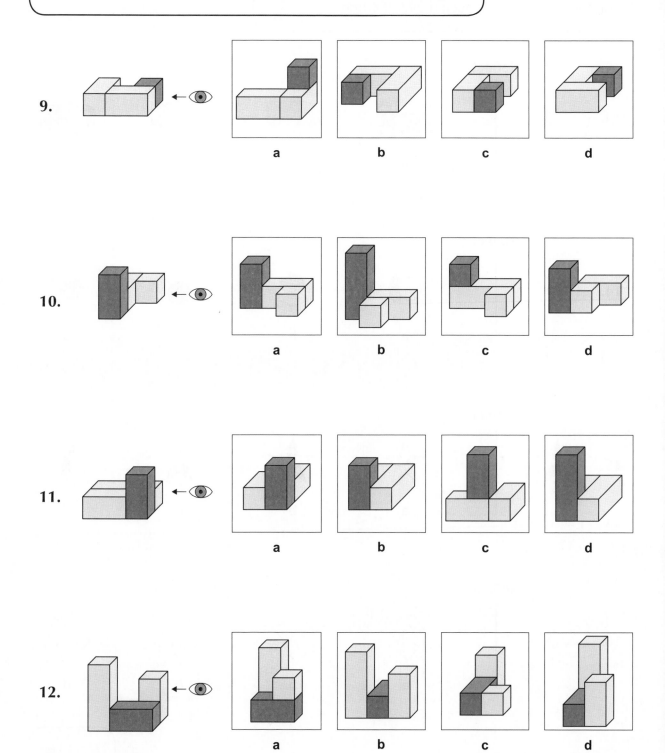

9.

a   b   c   d

10.

a   b   c   d

11.

a   b   c   d

12.

a   b   c   d

49

Work out which option would look like the figure on the left if it was reflected over the line.

Reflect

13.

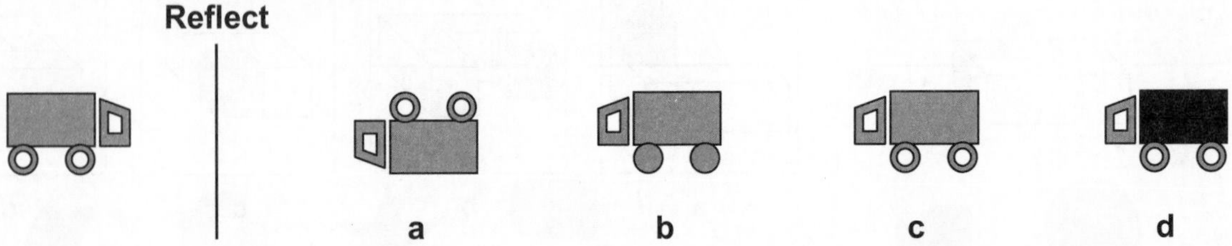

    a   b   c   d

Reflect

14.

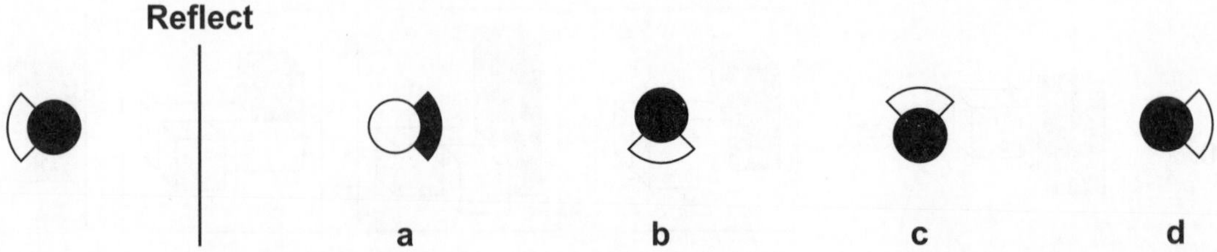

    a   b   c   d

Reflect

15.

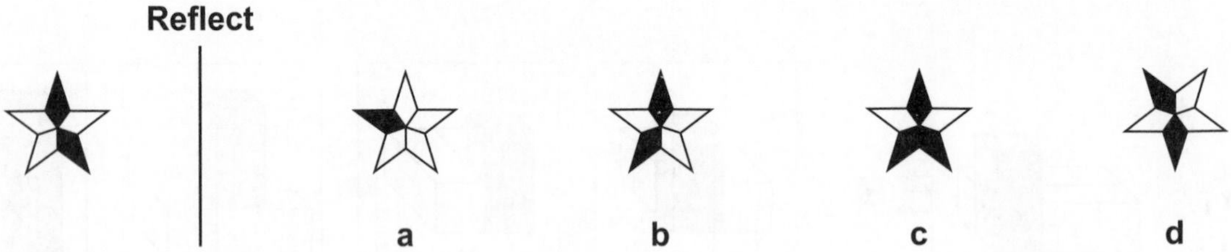

    a   b   c   d

Reflect

16.

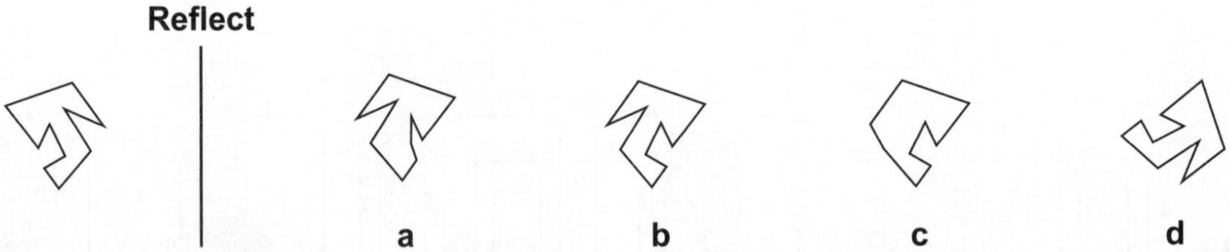

    a   b   c   d

/ 16

You have **10 minutes** to do this test. Circle the letter for each correct answer.

Work out which option is most like the two figures on the left.

1. |

                     a   **b**   **c**   **d**   **e**

2. |

                     a   **b**   **c**   **d**   **e**

3. |

                     a   **b**   **c**   **d**   **e**

4. |

                     a   **b**   **c**   **d**   **e**

51

Work out which option would look like the figure on the left if it was rotated.

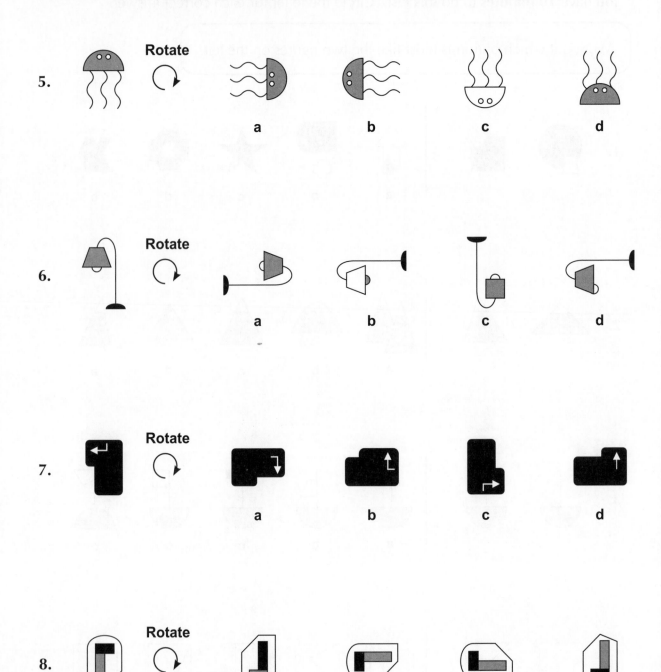

5. Rotate
       a   b   c   d

6. Rotate
       a   b   c   d

7. Rotate
       a   b   c   d

8. Rotate
       a   b   c   d

Work out which of the options best fits in place of the missing square in the grid.

9.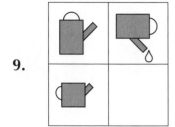

                                          a   b   c   d   e

10.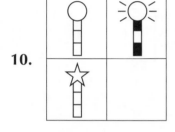

                                            a   b   c   d   e

11.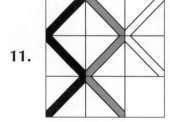

                                            a   b   c   d   e

12.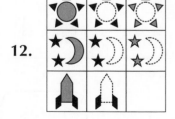

                                            a   b   c   d   e

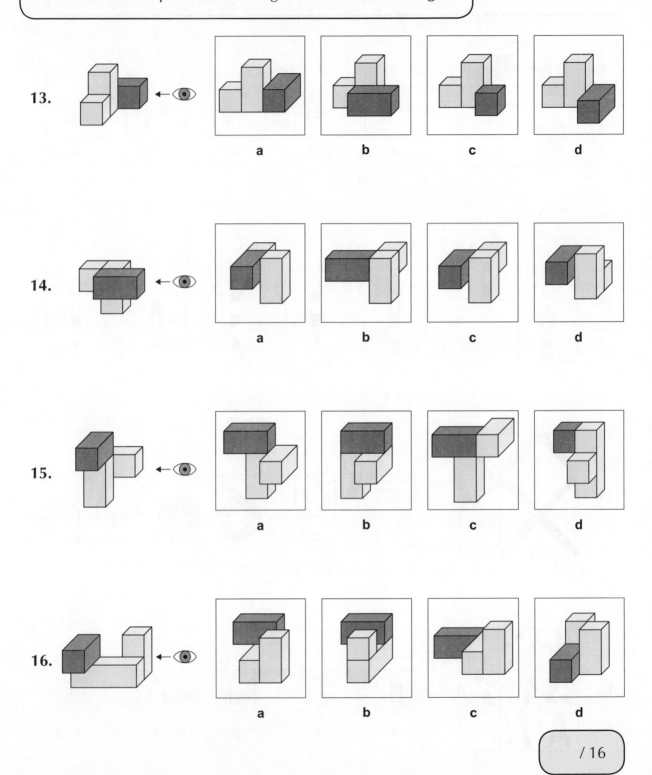

13.

a   b   c   d

14.

a   b   c   d

15.

a   b   c   d

16.

a   b   c   d

/ 16

54

You have **10 minutes** to do this test. Circle the letter for each correct answer.

Look at how the first figure is changed, and then work out which option would look like the second figure if you changed it in the same way.

1.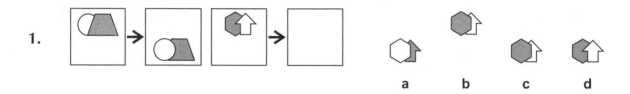

2.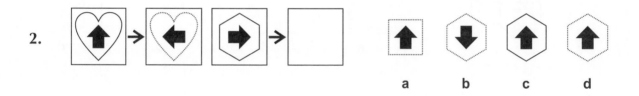

3.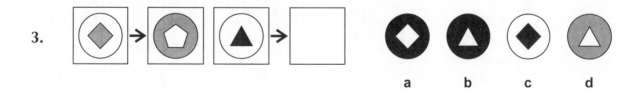

4.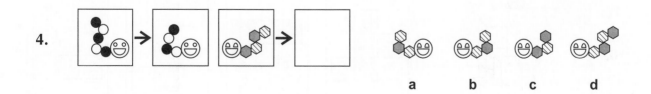

Work out which option is a top-down 2D view of the 3D figure on the left.

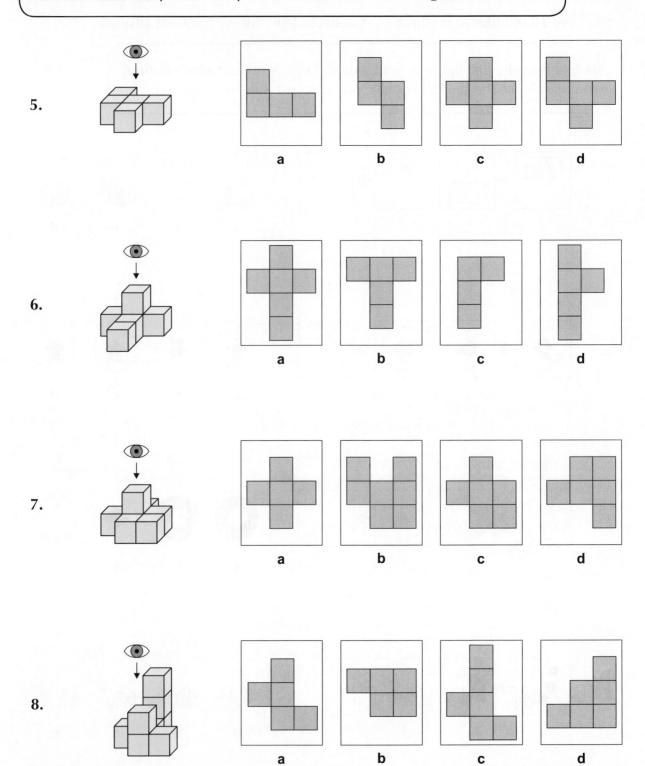

5.

a   b   c   d

6.

a   b   c   d

7.

a   b   c   d

8.

a   b   c   d

Find the figure in each row that is most unlike the others.

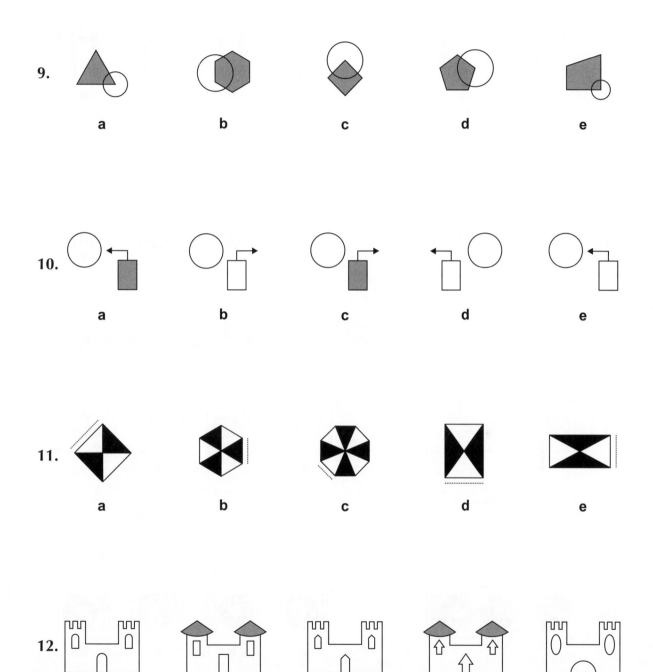

9.   a   b   c   d   e

10.   a   b   c   d   e

11.   a   b   c   d   e

12.   a   b   c   d   e

57

Work out which of the options best fits in place of the missing square in the series.

13.

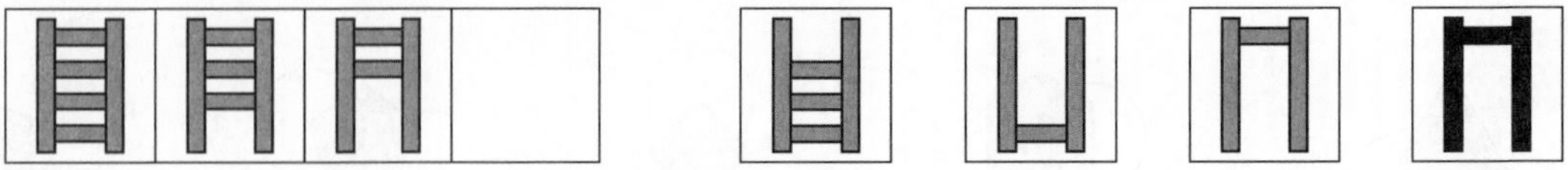

a   b   c   d

14.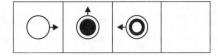

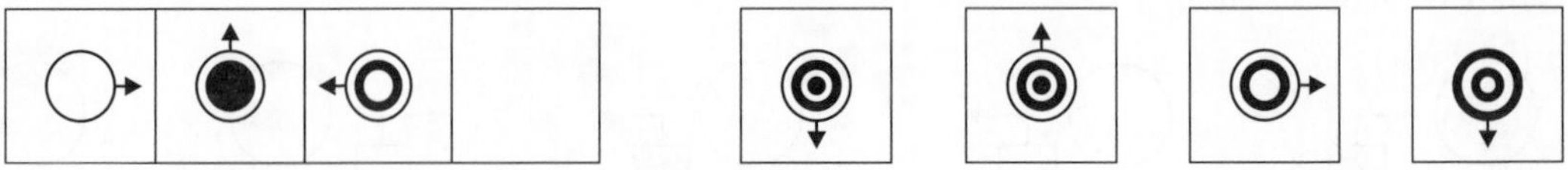

a   b   c   d

15.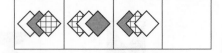

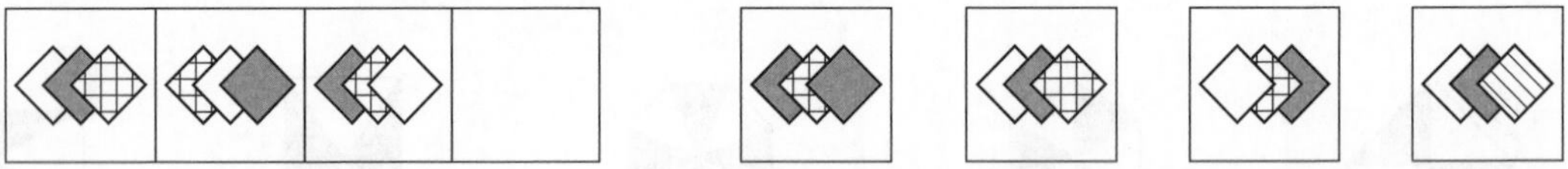

a   b   c   d

16.

a   b   c   d

/ 16

Puzzles 4

These puzzles are a brilliant way to practise some of the skills you'll need.

Puzzling Prints

Dan the Detective is trying to catch a robber.

He has found some footprints (marked A-E), but they're not complete.

Four belong to people that Dan knows. One belongs to the robber.

Match the bottom of each shoe to the correct footprint. Which footprint belongs to the robber?

Pat the Postman	Gwen the Gardener	Micky the Milkman	Brenda the Builder

A   B   C   D   E

The Odd Sheep Out

Fergus the Farmer has two different types of sheep on his farm.
He keeps each type of sheep in a separate field.
One sheep has escaped into the wrong field.
Which of the sheep below is the sheep that has escaped?

Puzzles 4

Test 13

You have **10 minutes** to do this test. Circle the letter for each correct answer.

Work out which option would look like the figure
on the left if it was reflected over the line.

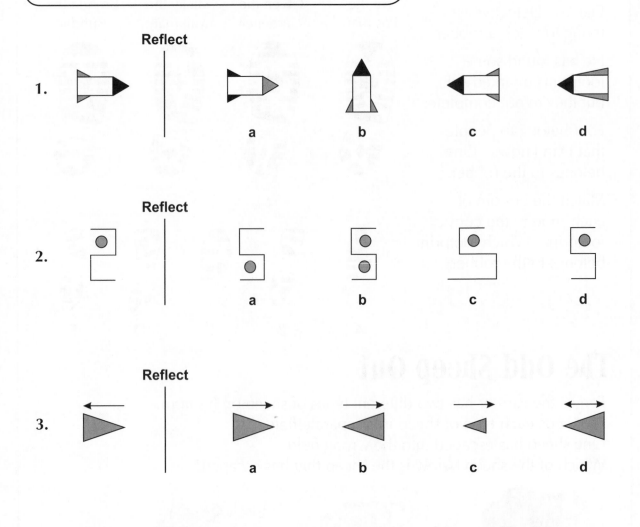

60

Work out which of the options best fits in place of the missing square in the series.

5. 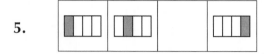

                                                 a   b   c   d

6. 

                                                 a   b   c   d

7. 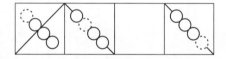

                                                 a   b   c   d

8. 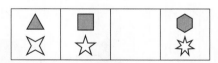

                                                 a   b   c   d

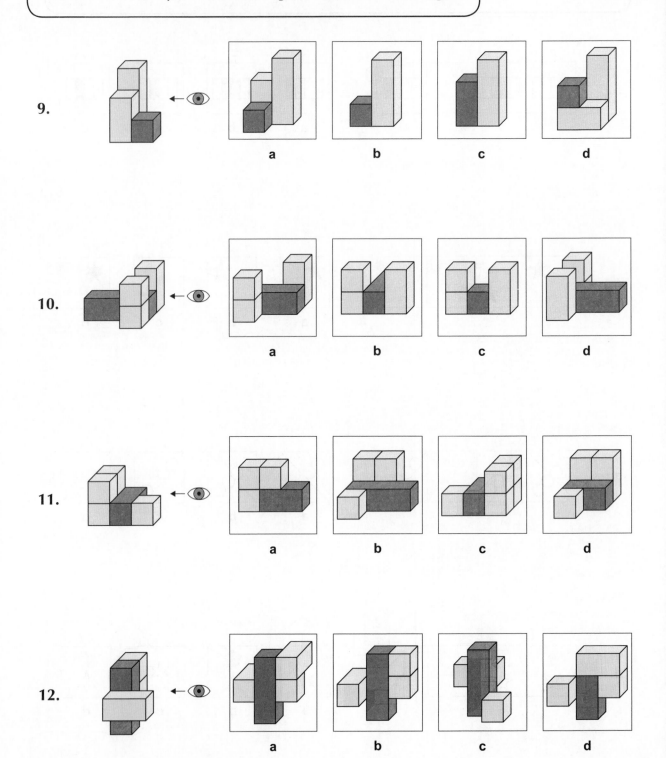

9.

a b c d

10.

a b c d

11.

a b c d

12.

a b c d

62

Work out which option is most like the two figures on the left.

13.

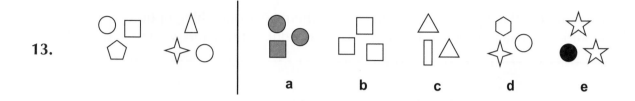

a   b   c   d   e

14.

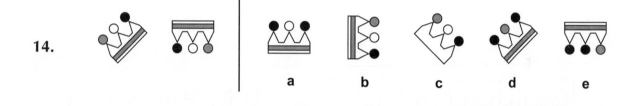

a   b   c   d   e

15.

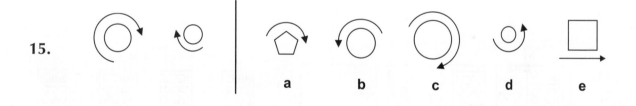

a   b   c   d   e

16.

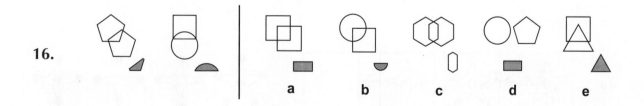

a   b   c   d   e

/ 16

63

You have **10 minutes** to do this test. Circle the letter for each correct answer.

Look at how the first figure is changed, and then work out which option would look like the second figure if you changed it in the same way.

1.

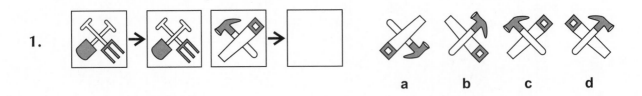

                  a   b   c   d

2.

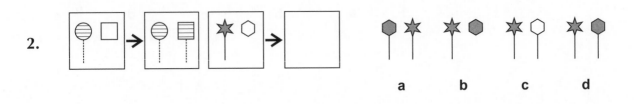

                  a   b   c   d

3.

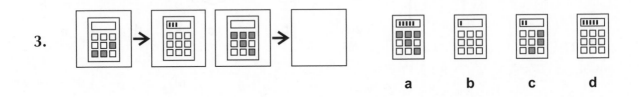

                  a   b   c   d

4.

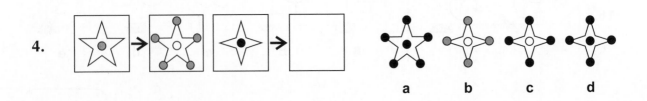

                  a   b   c   d

         64

Work out which of the options best fits in place of the missing square in the grid.

5.

a   b   c   d   e

6.

a   b   c   d   e

7.

a   b   c   d   e

8.

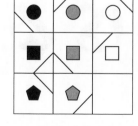

a   b   c   d   e

Test 14

Work out which option is most like the three figures on the left.

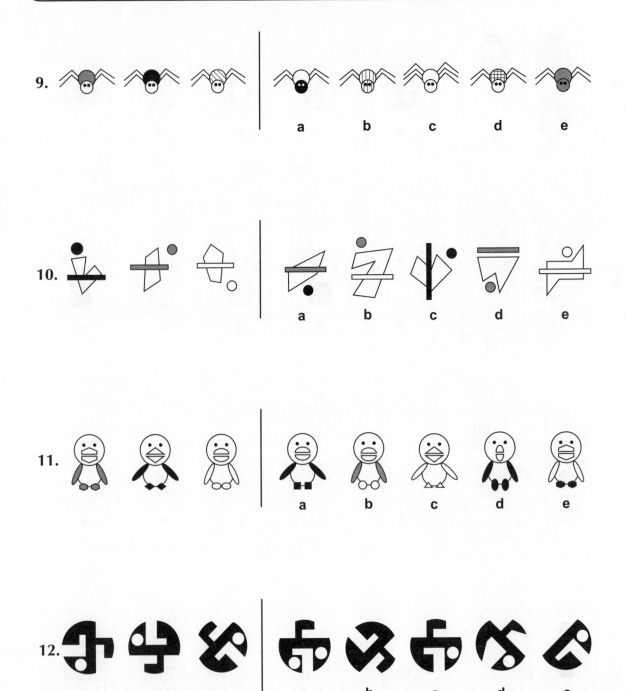

9.

     a   b   c   d   e

10.

     a   b   c   d   e

11.

     a   b   c   d   e

12.

     a   b   c   d   e

Work out which option is a top-down 2D view of the 3D figure on the left.

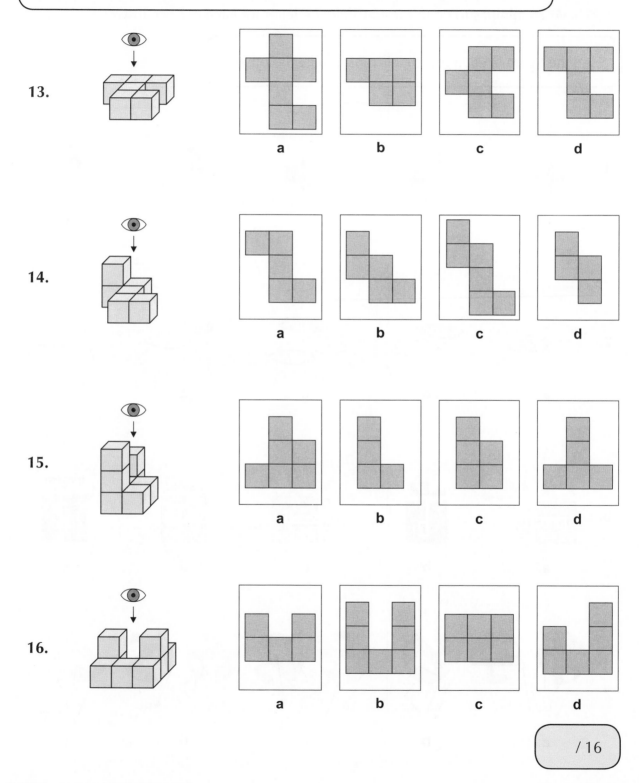

13.

a   b   c   d

14.

a   b   c   d

15.

a   b   c   d

16.

a   b   c   d

/ 16

67

You have **10 minutes** to do this test. Circle the letter for each correct answer.

Find the figure in each row that is most unlike the others.

1.

a   b   c   d   e

2.

a   b   c   d   e

3.

a   b   c   d   e

4.

a   b   c   d   e

      68

Work out which option would look like the figure on the left if it was rotated.

5.  **Rotate** ⟳

a

b

c

d

6. **Rotate** ⟳

a

b

c

d

7. **Rotate** ⟳

a

b

c

d

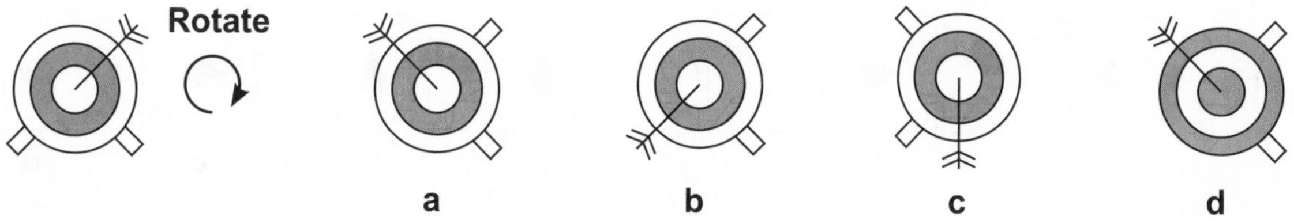

8. **Rotate** ⟳

a
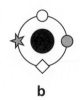
b

c

d

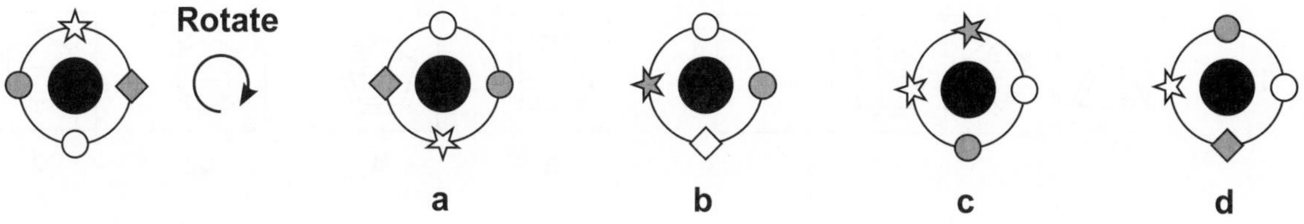

Test 15

Work out which of the options best fits in place of the missing square in the series.

9.

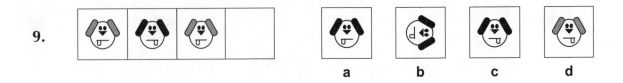

a   b   c   d

10.

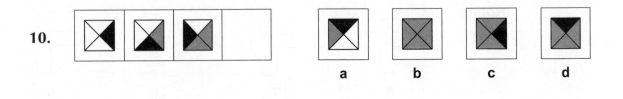

a   b   c   d

11.

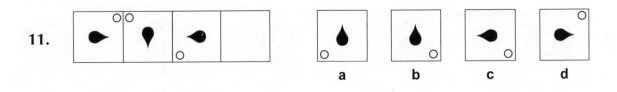

a   b   c   d

12.

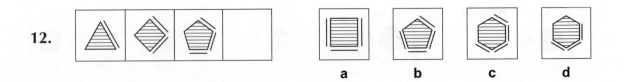

a   b   c   d

Look at how the first figure is changed, and then work out which option would look like the second figure if you changed it in the same way.

13.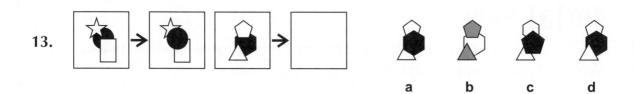

a   b   c   d

14.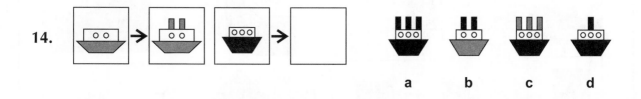

a   b   c   d

15.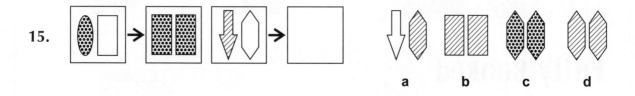

a   b   c   d

16.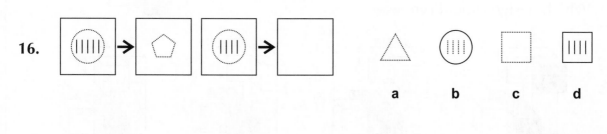

a   b   c   d

/ 16

71

Puzzles 5

Have a go at the puzzles on this page — they'll help you with your **3D shape** skills.

Aerial View

Noah is looking at a map of where he lives. His house is labelled below.
Which of the houses to the right of the map is Noah's?

Noah's house

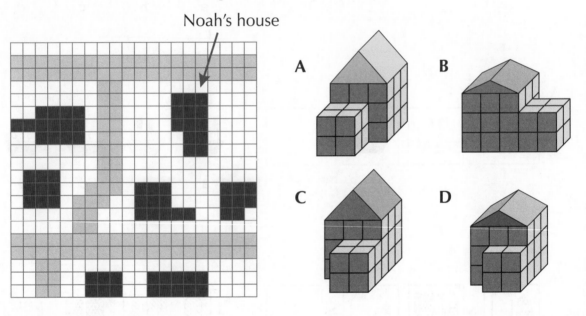

A

B

C

D

Fully Booked

Lyra is making some book ends using building blocks.
She has made this book end for one end of her shelf:

She wants the other book end to be a reflection of it.
Which design should Lyra use?

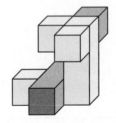

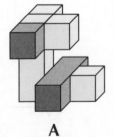

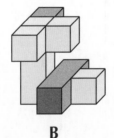

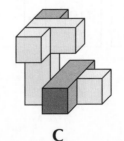

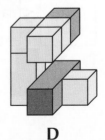

A   **B**   **C**   **D**

You have **10 minutes** to do this test. Circle the letter for each correct answer.

Work out which option is the 3D figure viewed from the **right**.

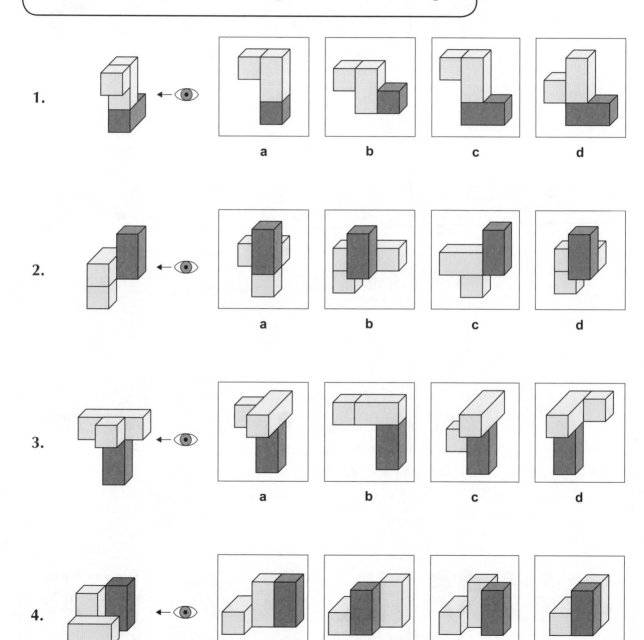

1.   a   b   c   d

2.   a   b   c   d

3.   a   b   c   d

4.   a   b   c   d

73

5.

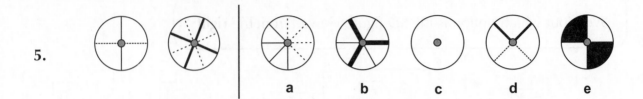

a   b   c   d   e

6.

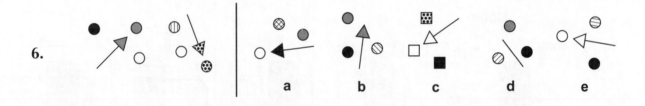

a   b   c   d   e

7.

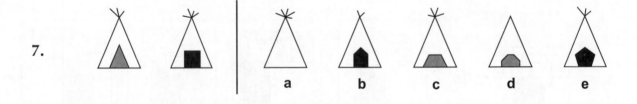

a   b   c   d   e

8.

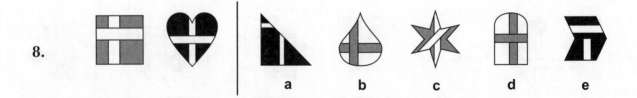

a   b   c   d   e

Work out which option would look like the figure on the left if it was rotated.

9.   **Rotate**

a   b   c   d

10.  **Rotate**

a   b   c   d

11. 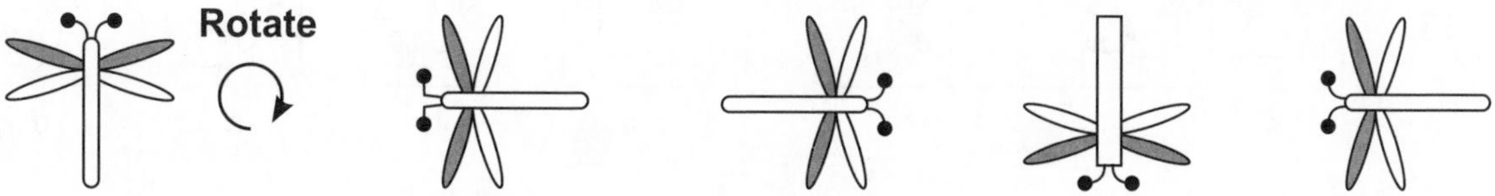  **Rotate**

a   b   c   d

12. **Rotate**

a   b   c   d

Test 16

Work out which of the options best fits in place of the missing square in the series.

13.

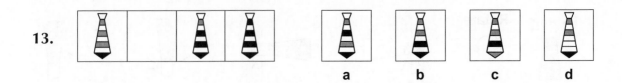

a   b   c   d

14.

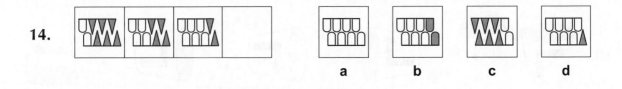

a   b   c   d

15.

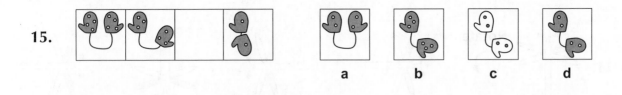

a   b   c   d

16.

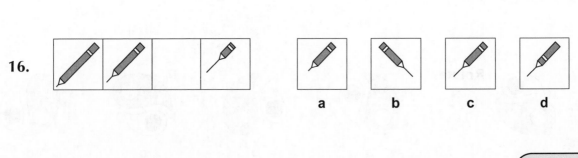

a   b   c   d

You have **10 minutes** to do this test. Circle the letter for each correct answer.

Work out which option is most like the three figures on the left.

1.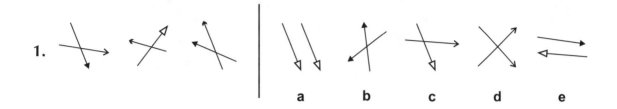

2.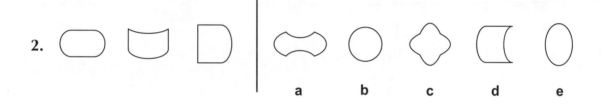

3.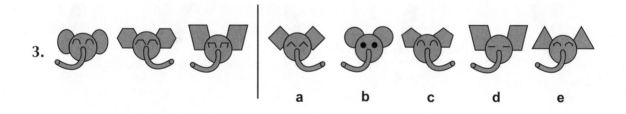

4.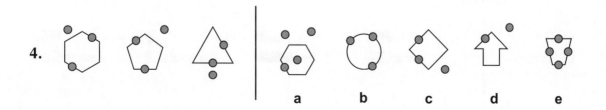

Test 17

Work out which option would look like the figure on the left if it was reflected over the line.

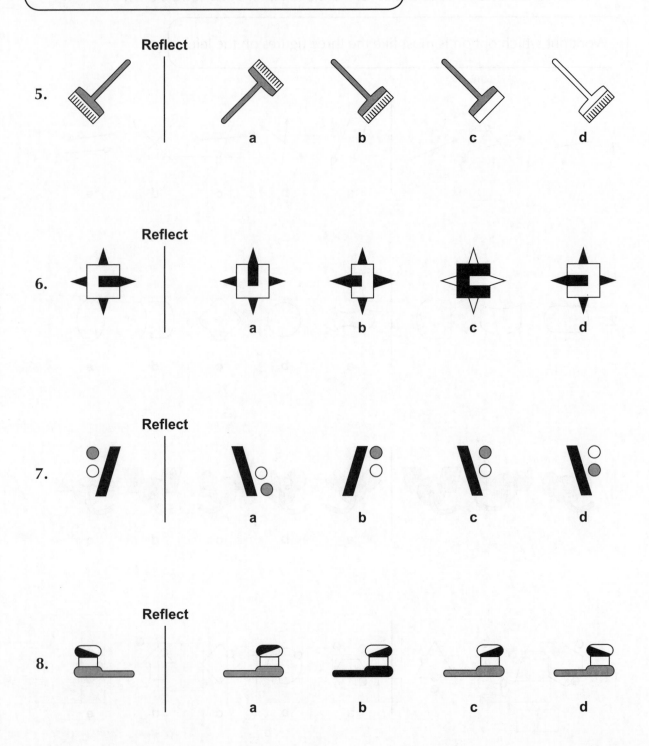

Reflect

5. a b c d

Reflect

6. a b c d

Reflect

7. a b c d

Reflect

8. a b c d

Work out which option is a top-down 2D view of the 3D figure on the left.

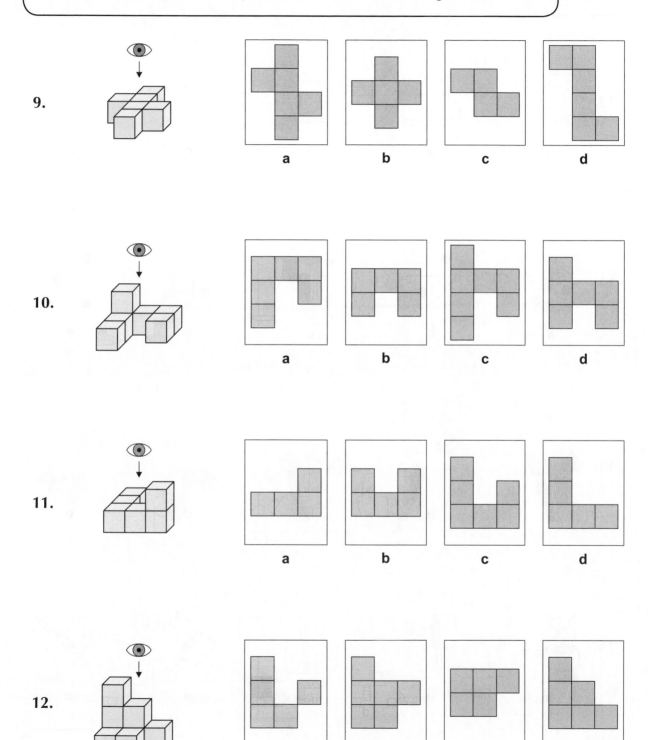

9.

a   b   c   d

10.

a   b   c   d

11.

a   b   c   d

12.

a   b   c   d

79

Find the figure in each row that is most unlike the others.

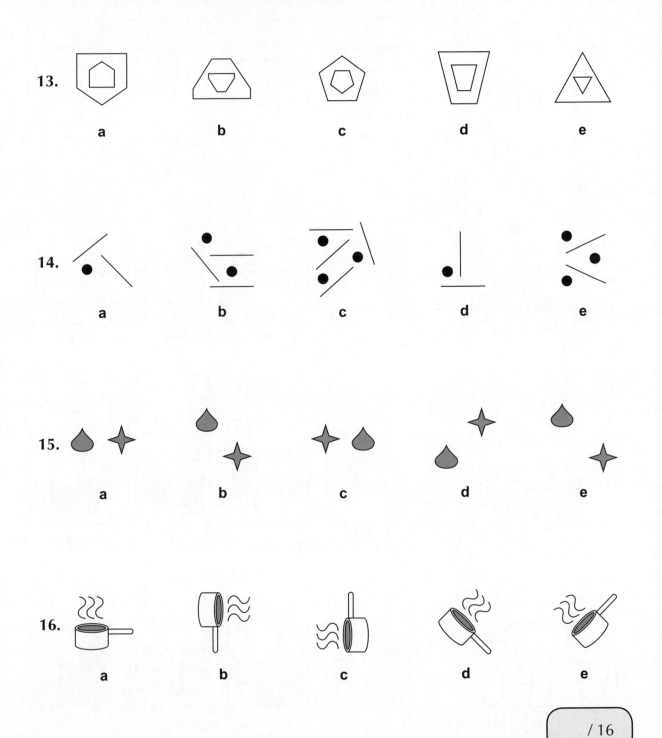

13.
a   b   c   d   e

14.
a   b   c   d   e

15.
a   b   c   d   e

16.
a   b   c   d   e

/ 16

You have **10 minutes** to do this test. Circle the letter for each correct answer.

Work out which option would look like the figure on the left if it was rotated.

1.

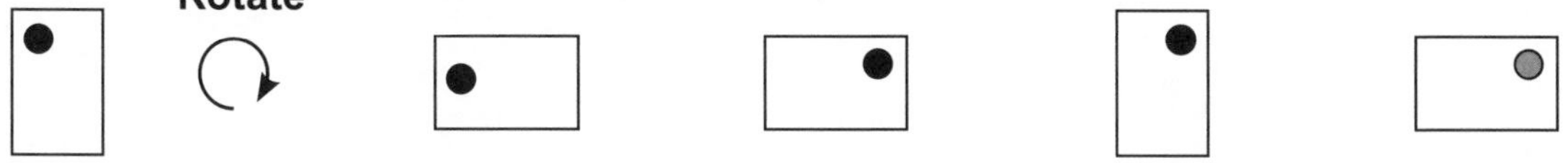

          a   **b**   **c**   **d**

2.

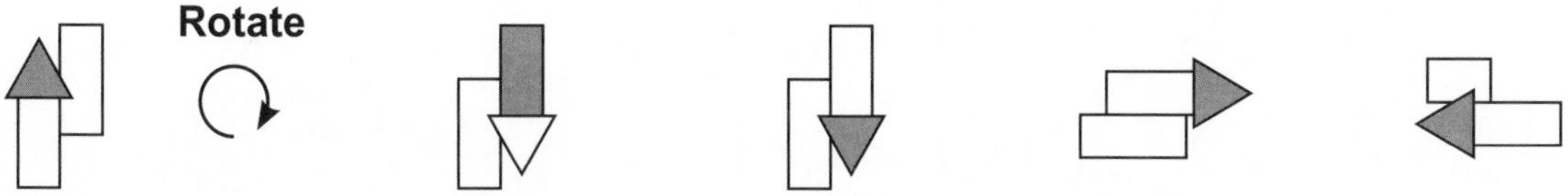

          a   **b**   **c**   **d**

3.

          a   **b**   **c**   **d**

4.

          a   **b**   **c**   **d**

Work out which option is most like the three figures on the left.

5.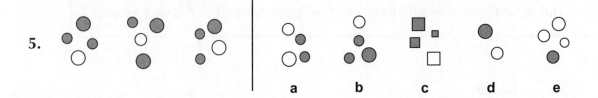

| a | b | c | d | e |

6.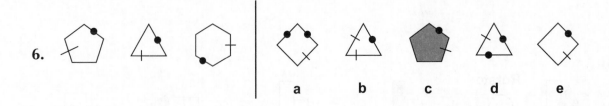

| a | b | c | d | e |

7.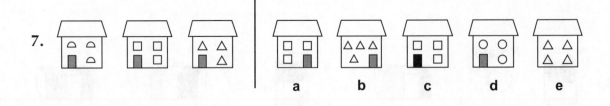

| a | b | c | d | e |

8.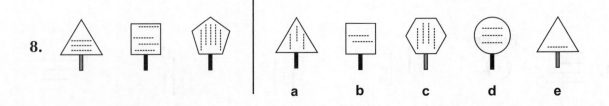

| a | b | c | d | e |

82

Work out which of the options best fits in place of the missing square in the grid.

9.

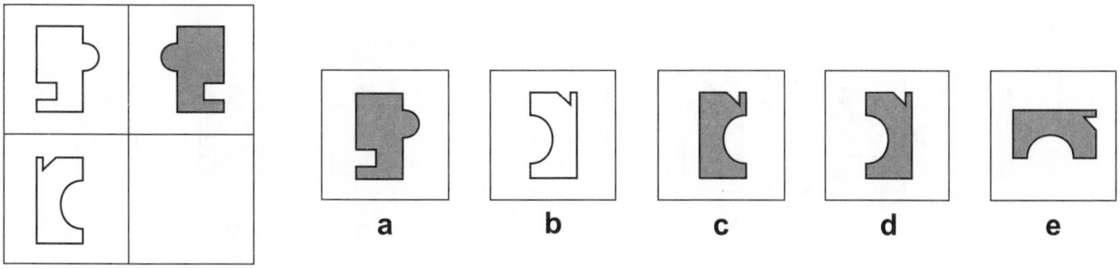

a   b   c   d   e

10.

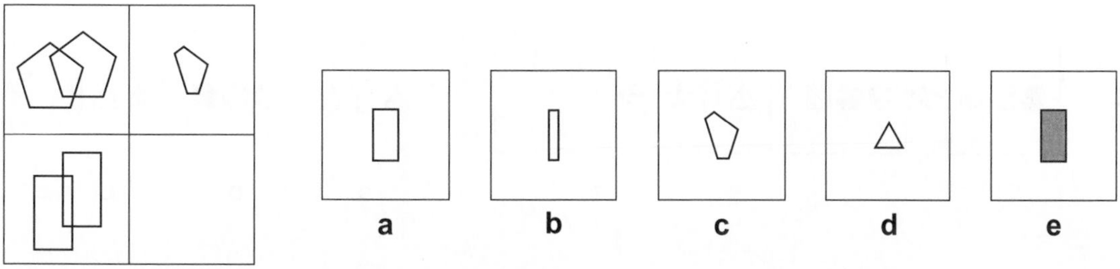

a   b   c   d   e

11.

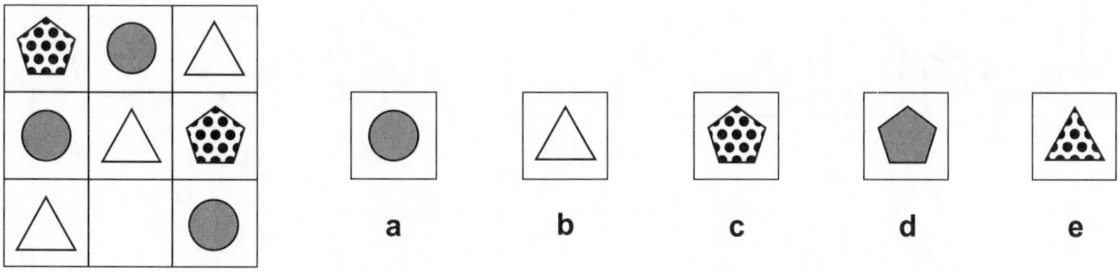

a   b   c   d   e

12.

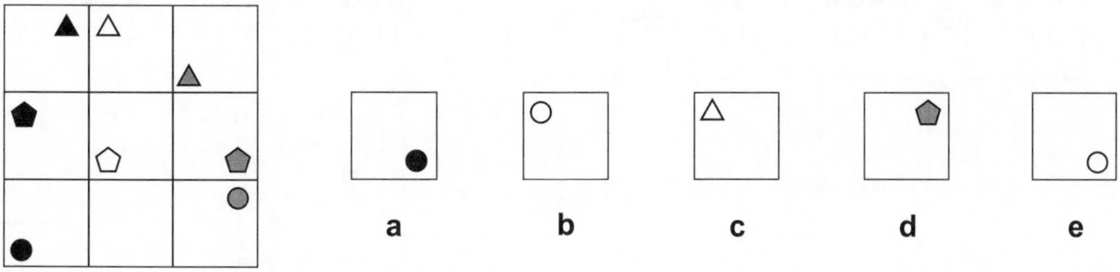

a   b   c   d   e

83

Look at how the first figure is changed, and then work out which option would look like the second figure if you changed it in the same way.

13.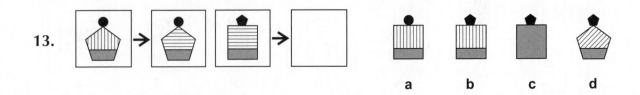

| a | b | c | d |

14.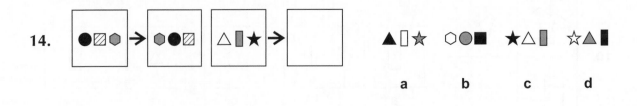

| a | b | c | d |

15.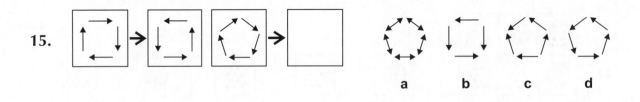

| a | b | c | d |

16.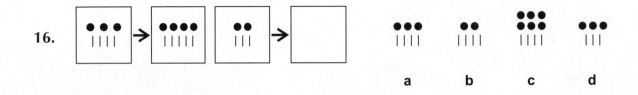

| a | b | c | d |

/ 16

It's puzzle time! This page will help you practise **spotting links** and **rotating shapes**.

Improve My Ride

Eric has made some improvements to his car. Eric's friend Kevin wants similar improvements making to his car. On the blank car below, draw what Kevin's car will look like if it changes in the same way.

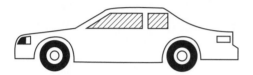

Eric's car before

Eric's car after

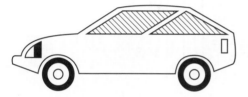

Kevin's car before

Kevin's car after

Shell Shapes

Last week, Hamish painted shapes onto Samantha the Snail's shell so he could keep track of her in his garden. Today, he has found four snails asleep in their shells, but can't work out which shell belongs to Samantha. Circle Samantha's shell.

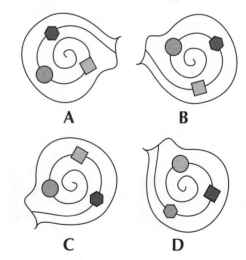

Test 19

You have **10 minutes** to do this test. Circle the letter for each correct answer.

Work out which option is the 3D figure viewed from the **right**.

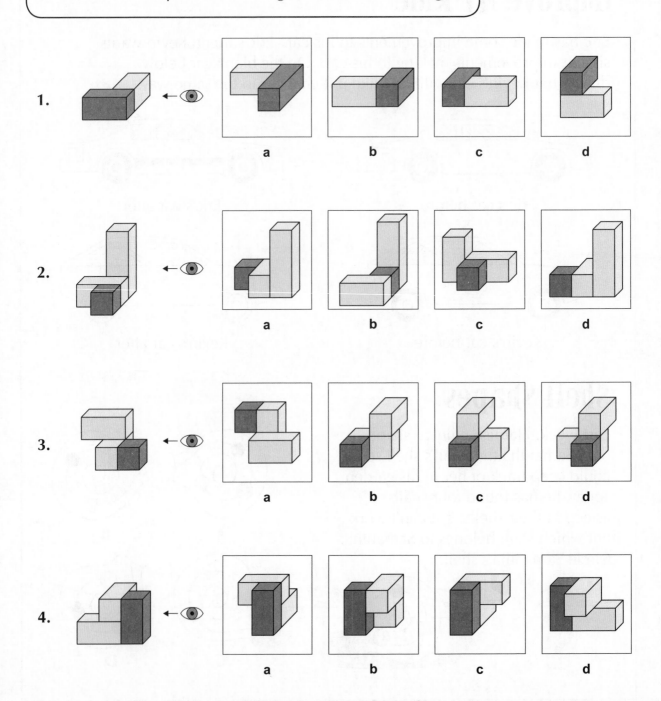

1.

    a   b   c   d

2.

    a   b   c   d

3.

    a   b   c   d

4.

    a   b   c   d

86

Find the figure in each row that is most unlike the others.

5.

    a   b   c   d   e

6.

    a   b   c   d   e

7.

    a   b   c   d   e

8.

    a   b   c   d   e

87

Test 19

Look at how the first figure is changed, and then work out which option would look like the second figure if you changed it in the same way.

9.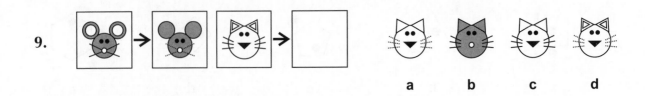

a   b   c   d

10.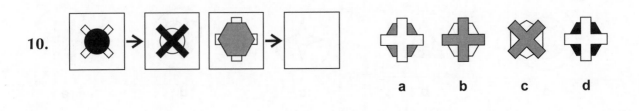

a   b   c   d

11.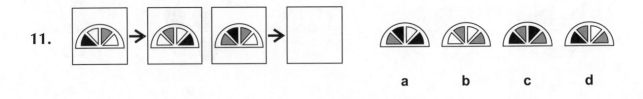

a   b   c   d

12.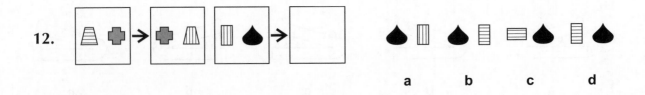

a   b   c   d

Work out which of the options best fits in place of the missing square in the series.

13.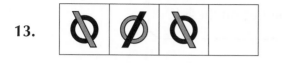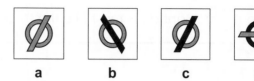

a   b   c   d

14.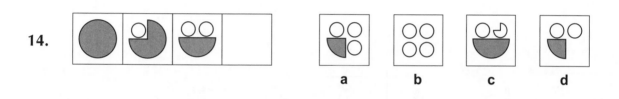

a   b   c   d

15.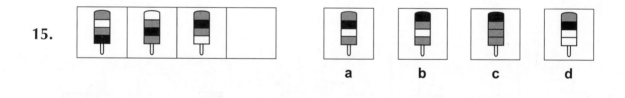

a   b   c   d

16.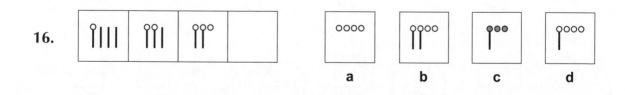

a   b   c   d

/ 16

89

Test 20

You have **10 minutes** to do this test. Circle the letter for each correct answer.

Work out which option is most like the three figures on the left.

1. |

                                              a   **b**   **c**   **d**   **e**

2. |

                                              a   **b**   **c**   **d**   **e**

3. |

                                              a   **b**   **c**   **d**   **e**

4. |

                                              a   **b**   **c**   **d**   **e**

Work out which option would look like the figure on the left if it was reflected over the line.

Reflect

5. 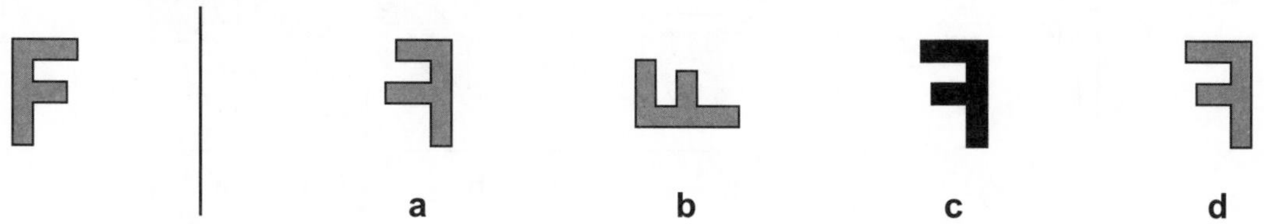
a   b   c   d

Reflect

6. 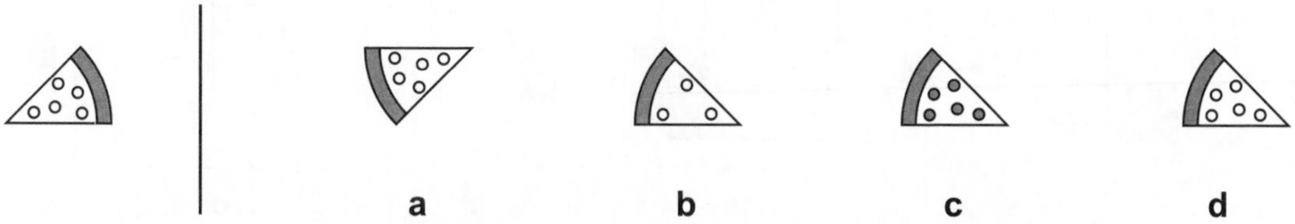
a   b   c   d

Reflect

7. 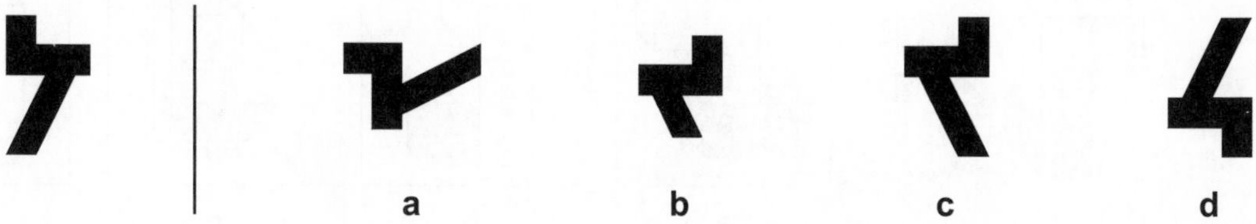
a   b   c   d

Reflect

8. 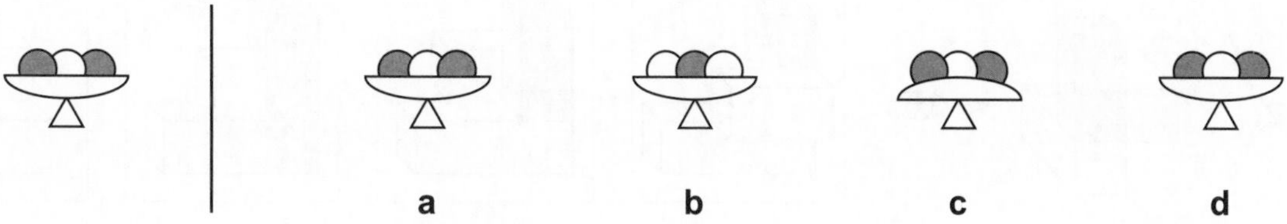
a   b   c   d

91

Work out which option is the 3D figure viewed from the **right**.

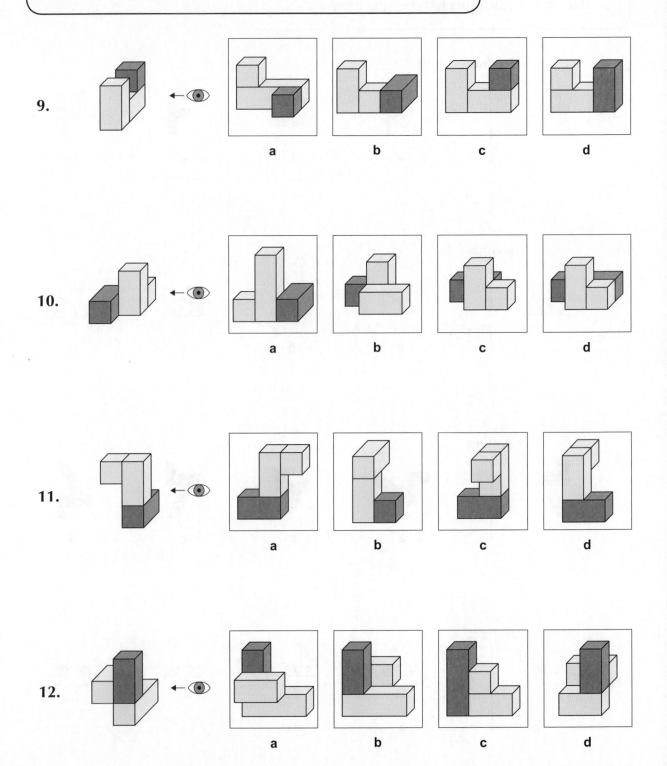

9.

10.

11.

12.

92

Work out which of the options best fits in place of the missing square in the grid.

13.

      a   **b**   **c**   **d**   **e**

14.

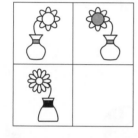

      a   **b**   **c**   **d**   **e**

15.

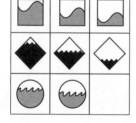

      a   **b**   **c**   **d**   **e**

16.

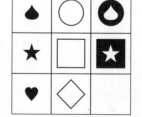

      a   **b**   **c**   **d**   **e**

/ 16

93

You have **10 minutes** to do this test. Circle the letter for each correct answer.

Find the figure in each row that is most unlike the others.

1.

    a   **b**   **c**   **d**   **e**

2.

    a   **b**   **c**   **d**   **e**

3.

    a   **b**   **c**   **d**   **e**

4.

    a   **b**   **c**   **d**   **e**

Work out which option is most like the two figures on the left.

5.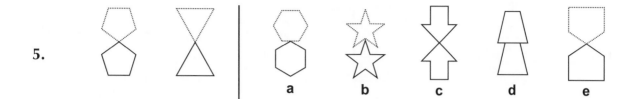

6.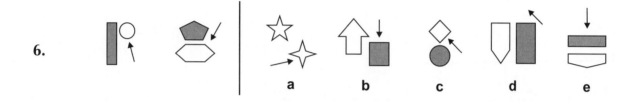

7.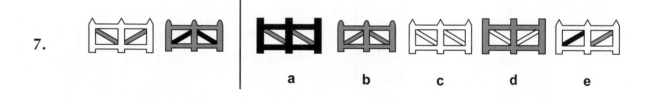

8.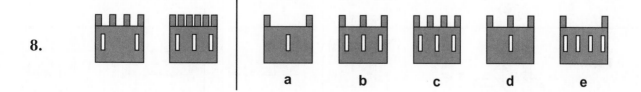

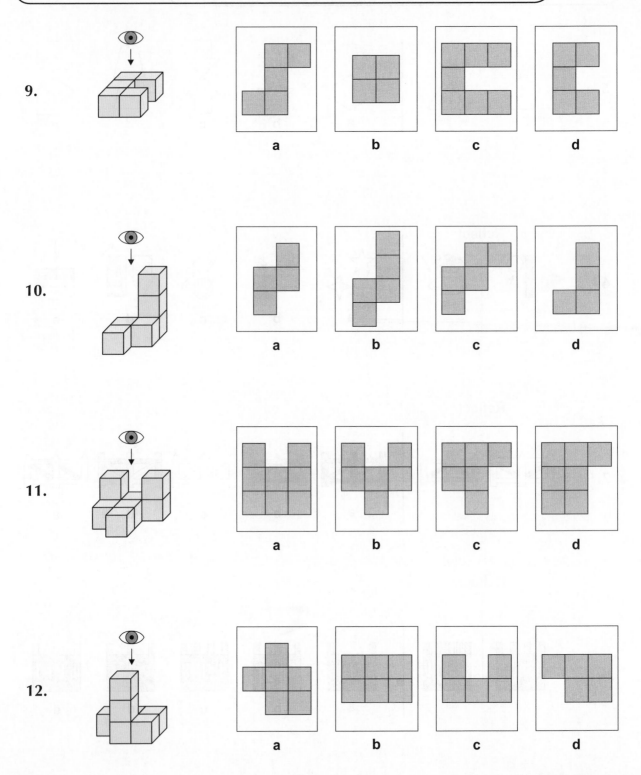

9.

a   b   c   d

10.

a   b   c   d

11.

a   b   c   d

12.

a   b   c   d

96

Work out which option would look like the figure on the left if it was reflected over the line.

Reflect

13.

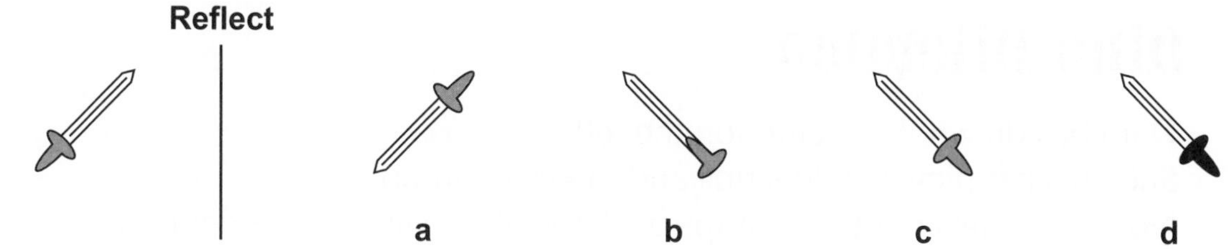

a b c d

Reflect

14.

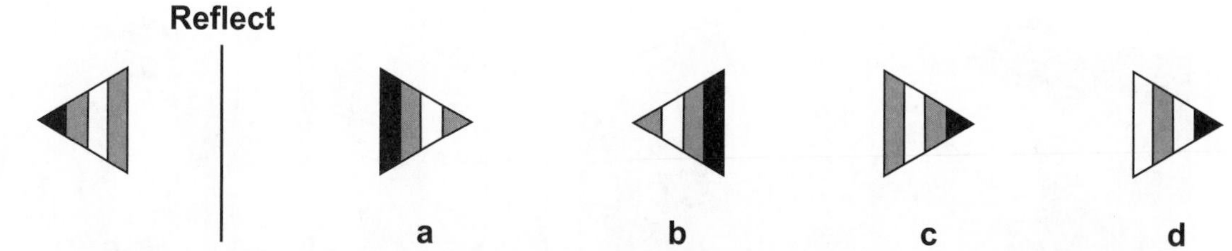

a b c d

Reflect

15.

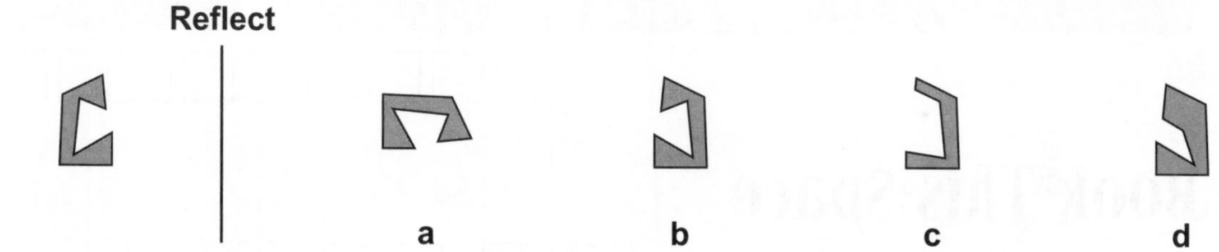

a b c d

Reflect

16.

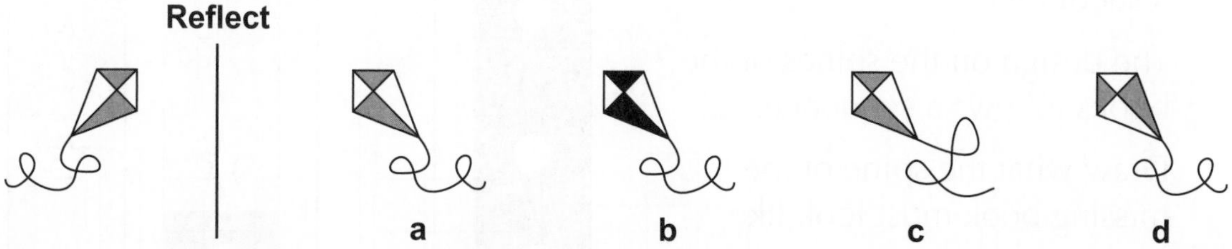

a b c d

/ 16

97

Puzzles 7

Break time! These puzzles are perfect for practising your skills with **sequences**.

Dino Dilemma

Dani has drawn the picture on the left.
She cuts her picture into strips and mixes them up.
Now she wants to put the strips back together again in the right order.

Help Dani complete her picture by numbering the strips below from 1-10.
1 should be the far left of the picture and 10 should be the far right.

☐ ☐ ☐ ☐ ☐ ☐ ☐ ☐ ☐ ☐

Book This Space

Max is looking at his bookshelf.

He is missing one book from a set of four.

The design on the spines of the books follows a sequence.

Draw what the spine of the missing book must look like.

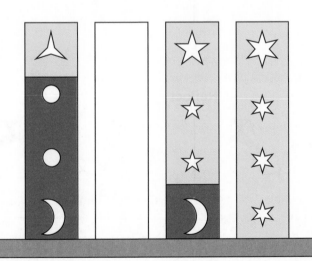

Test 22

You have **10 minutes** to do this test. Circle the letter for each correct answer.

Look at how the first figure is changed, and then work out which option would look like the second figure if you changed it in the same way.

1.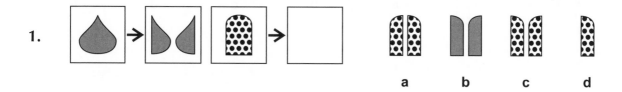

2.

3.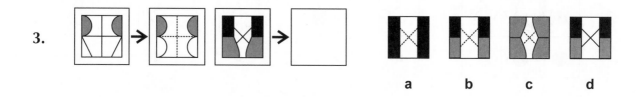

4.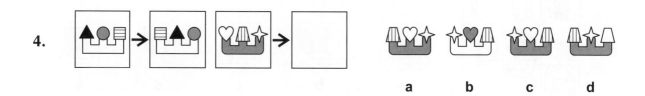

Work out which of the options best fits in place of the missing square in the grid.

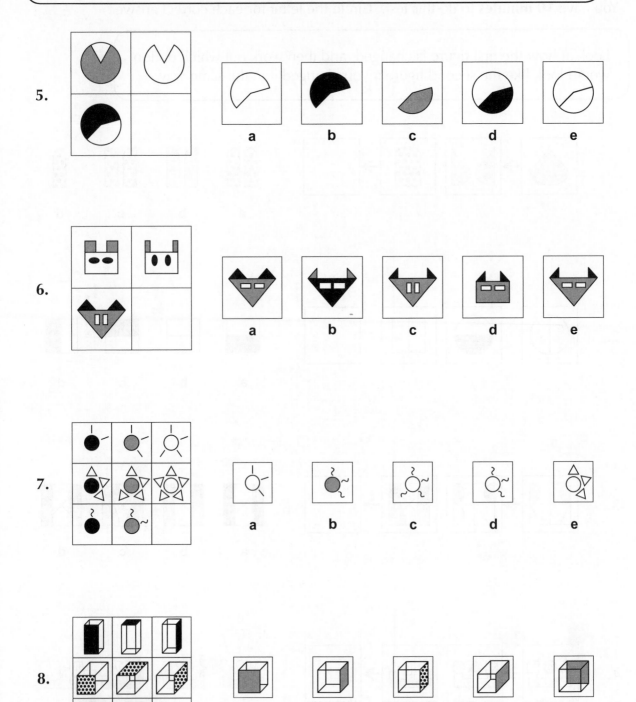

5.

    a   b   c   d   e

6.

    a   b   c   d   e

7.

    a   b   c   d   e

8.

    a   b   c   d   e

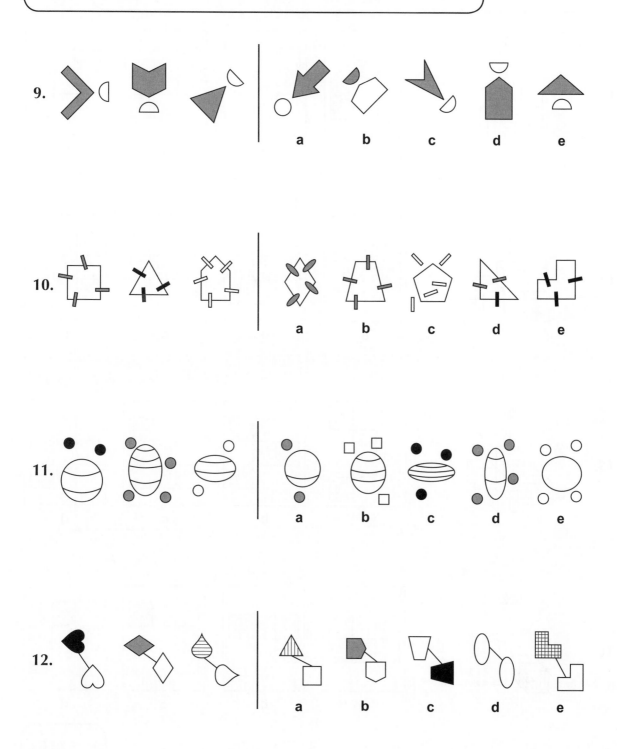

Work out which option is a top-down 2D view of the 3D figure on the left.

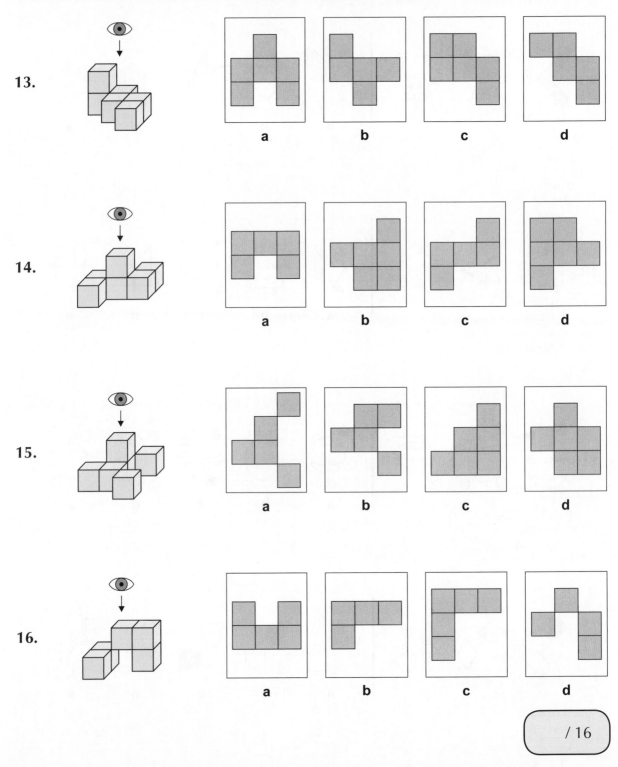

13.

a   b   c   d

14.

a   b   c   d

15.

a   b   c   d

16.

a   b   c   d

/ 16

Test 23

You have **10 minutes** to do this test. Circle the letter for each correct answer.

> Work out which option is most like the two figures on the left.

1.

           a   **b**   **c**   **d**   **e**

2.

           a   **b**   **c**   **d**   **e**

3.

           a   **b**   **c**   **d**   **e**

4.

           a   **b**   **c**   **d**   **e**

Work out which option would look like the figure on the left if it was rotated.

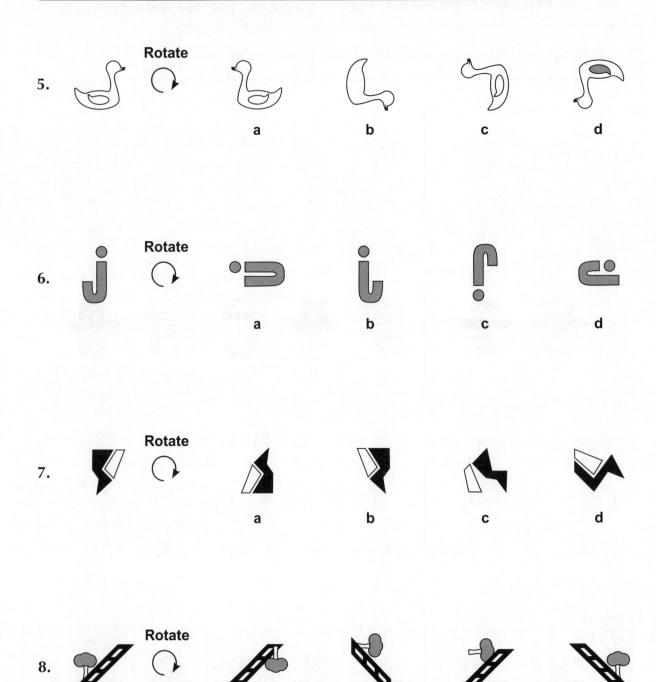

5.   Rotate

      a   b   c   d

6.   Rotate

      a   b   c   d

7.   Rotate

      a   b   c   d

8.   Rotate

      a   b   c   d

Work out which of the options best fits in place of the missing square in the series.

9.

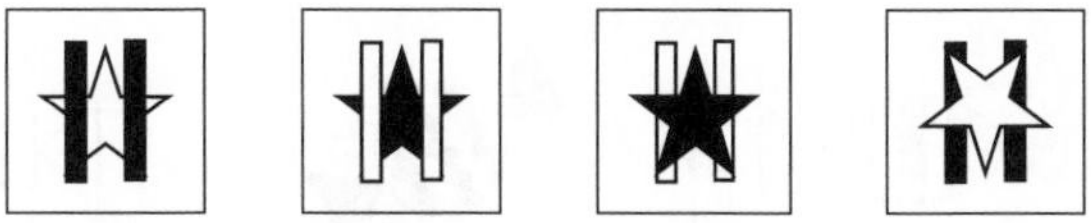

a   b   c   d

10.

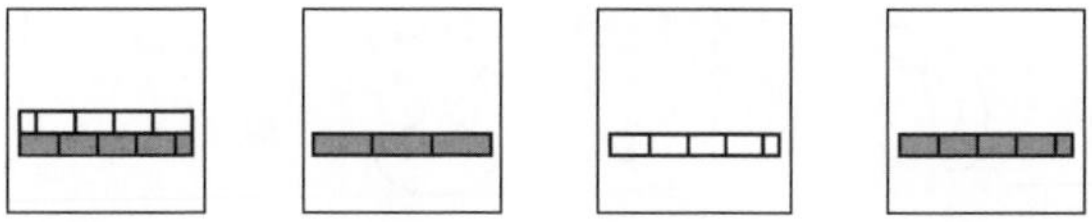

a   b   c   d

11.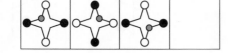

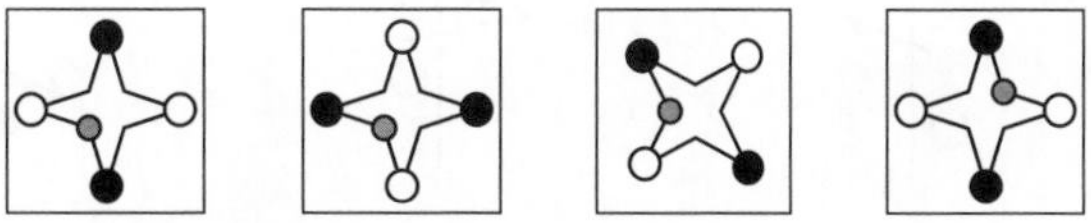

a   b   c   d

12.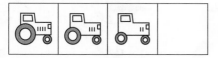

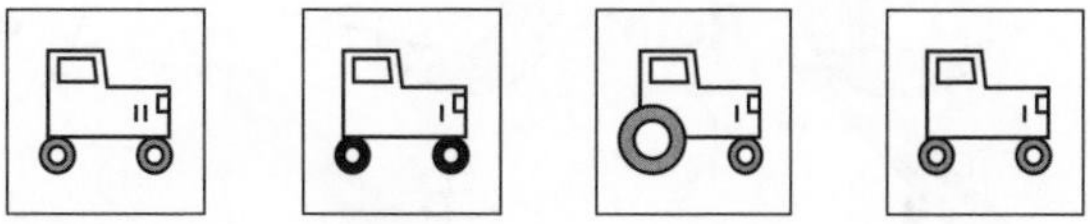

a   b   c   d

105   Test 23

Find the figure in each row that is most unlike the others.

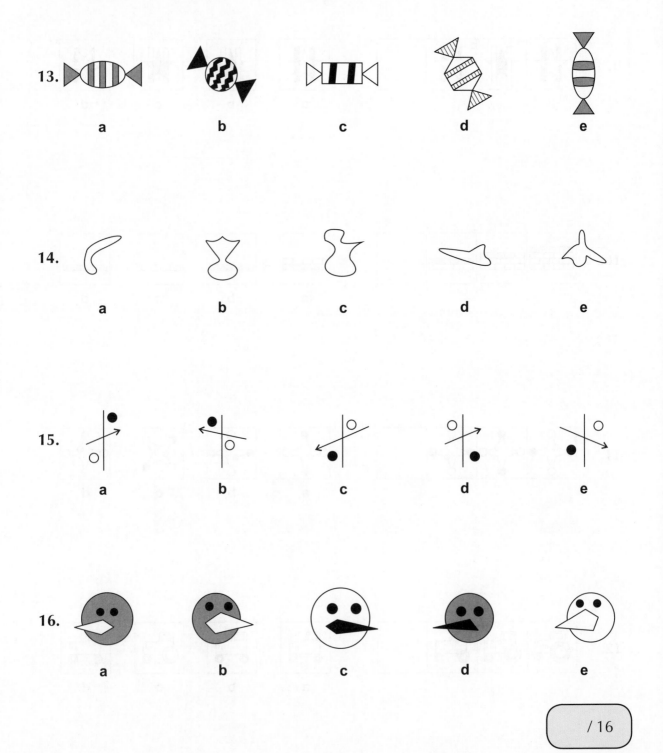

13.   a   b   c   d   e

14.   a   b   c   d   e

15.   a   b   c   d   e

16.   a   b   c   d   e

/ 16

Test 24

You have **10 minutes** to do this test. Circle the letter for each correct answer.

Work out which option would look like the figure on the left if it was reflected over the line.

Reflect

1.

     a   **b**   **c**   **d**

Reflect

2.

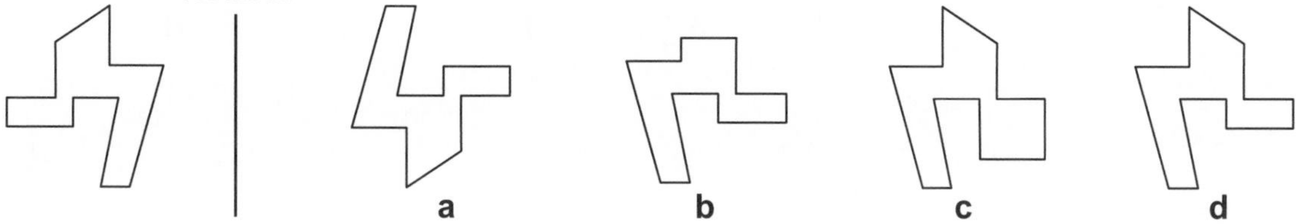

     a   **b**   **c**   **d**

Reflect

3.

     a   **b**   **c**   **d**

Reflect

4.

     a   **b**   **c**   **d**

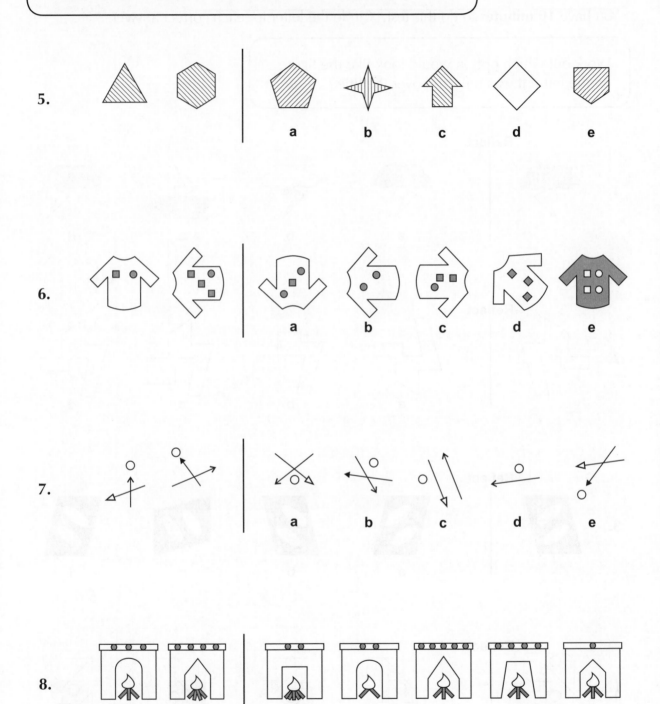

5.

6.

7.

8.

108

Work out which option is the 3D figure viewed from the **right**.

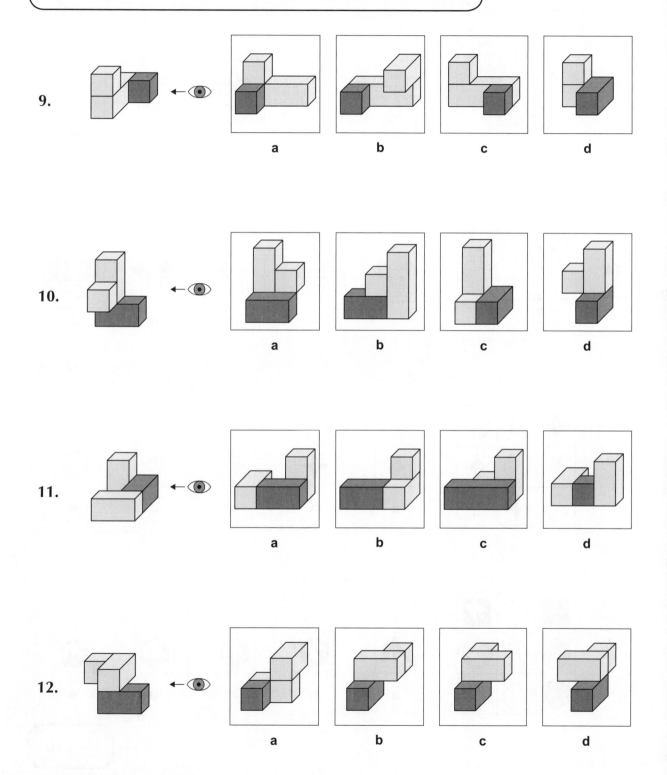

9.

a   b   c   d

10.

a   b   c   d

11.

a   b   c   d

12.

a   b   c   d

Test 24

Work out which of the options best fits in place of the missing square in the grid.

13.

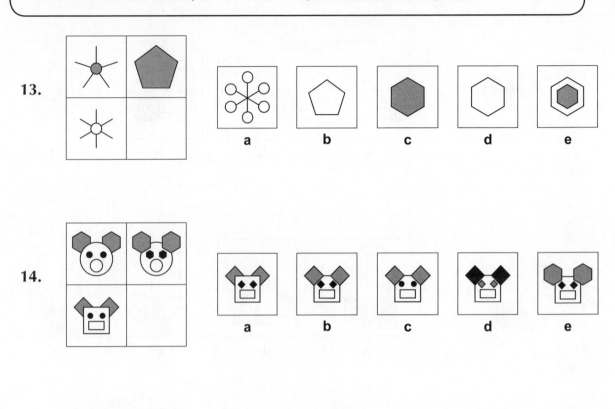

14.

15.

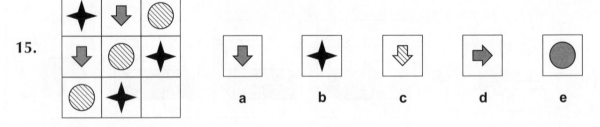

16.

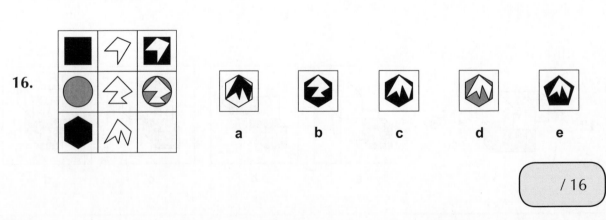

/ 16

110

Puzzles 8

Phew... Time for some puzzles to help you practise your **rotation** and **comparison** skills.

Art Attack

Some of Alan's paintings have had pieces cut out of them by a rival artist.
Which of the pieces below are from Alan's painting?
Some pieces may need rotating to fit back in the painting.
Draw lines to match the four gaps in the painting to the correct missing pieces.

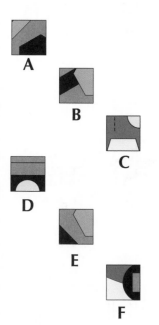
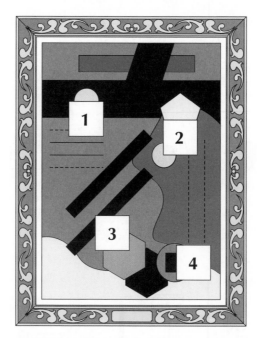
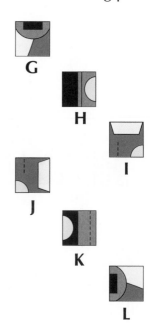

Location, Location, Location

Sadiq has just moved house.
He chose it because it is the
house most unlike the others
on its street.

Circle Sadiq's house.

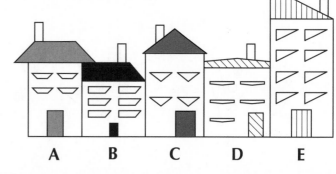

Test 25

You have **10 minutes** to do this test. Circle the letter for each correct answer.

Work out which option is most like the three figures on the left.

1.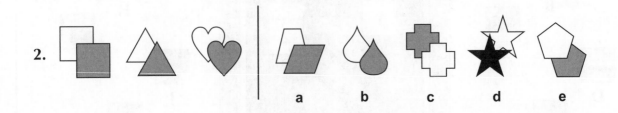

2.

3.

4.

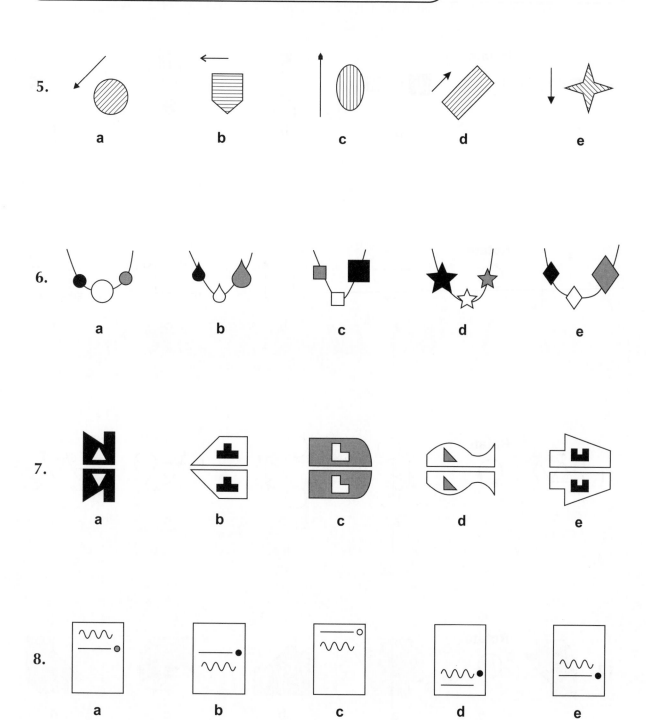

Find the figure in each row that is most unlike the others.

5.

   a   b   c   d   e

6.

   a   b   c   d   e

7.

   a   b   c   d   e

8.

   a   b   c   d   e

113

Work out which option would look like the figure on the left if it was rotated.

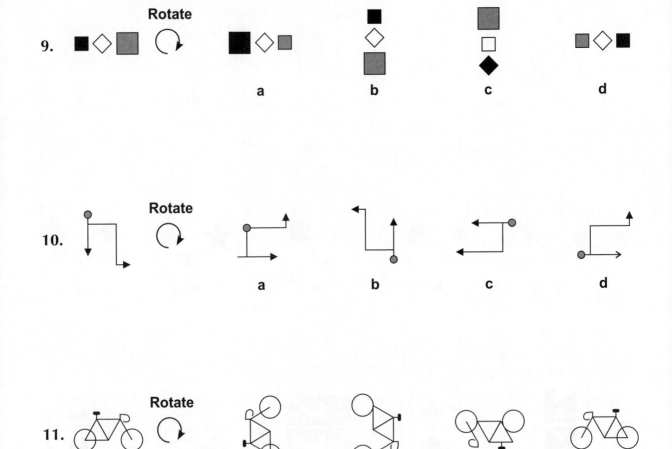

9.

Rotate

a b c d

10.

Rotate

a b c d

11.

Rotate

a b c d

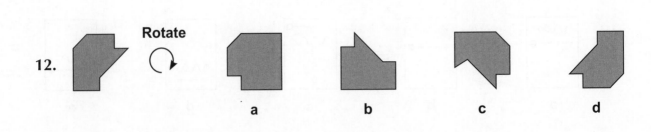

12.

Rotate

a b c d

114

13.

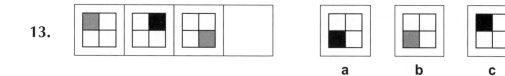

a   b   c   d

14.

a   b   c   d

15.

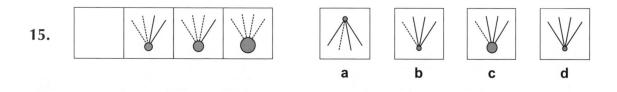

a   b   c   d

16.

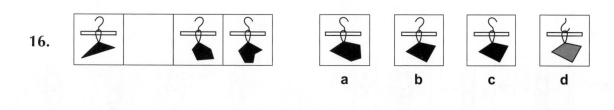

a   b   c   d

/ 16

Test 25

Test 26

You have **10 minutes** to do this test. Circle the letter for each correct answer.

Look at how the first figure is changed, and then work out which option would look like the second figure if you changed it in the same way.

1.

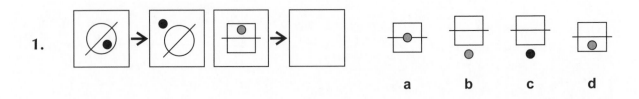

a   b   c   d

2.

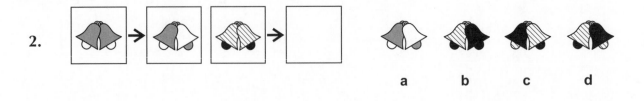

a   b   c   d

3.

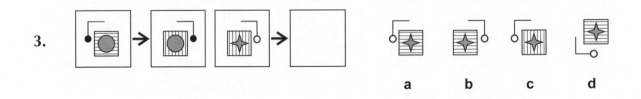

a   b   c   d

4.

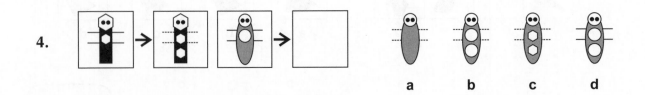

a   b   c   d

116

Work out which option would look like the figure on the left if it was reflected over the line.

5.

Reflect

a

b

c

d

6.

Reflect

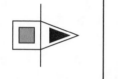

a

b

c

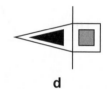

d

7.

Reflect

a

b

c

d

8.

Reflect

a

b

c

d

Test 26

Work out which option is most like the two figures on the left.

9.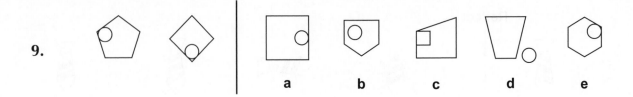

a   b   c   d   e

10.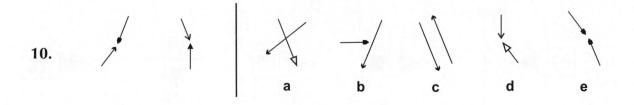

a   b   c   d   e

11.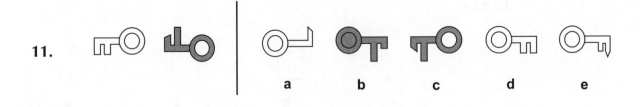

a   b   c   d   e

12.

a   b   c   d   e

Work out which option is a top-down 2D view of the 3D figure on the left.

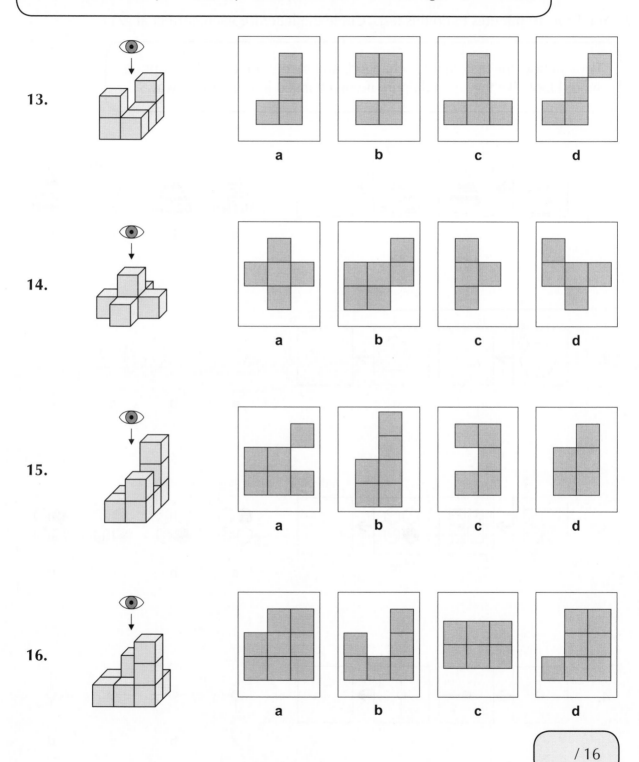

13.

a   b   c   d

14.

a   b   c   d

15.

a   b   c   d

16.

a   b   c   d

/ 16

119

You have **10 minutes** to do this test. Circle the letter for each correct answer.

Look at how the first figure is changed, and then work out which option would look like the second figure if you changed it in the same way.

1.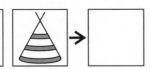

                                        a   **b**   **c**   **d**

2.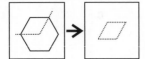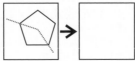

                                          a   **b**   **c**   **d**

3.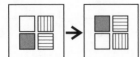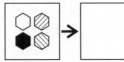

                                          a   **b**   **c**   **d**

4.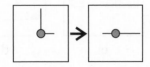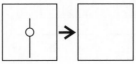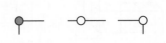

                                          a   **b**   **c**   **d**

Work out which of the options best fits in place of the missing square in the grid.

5.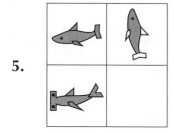

     a   **b**   **c**   **d**   **e**

6.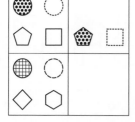

     a   **b**   **c**   **d**   **e**

7.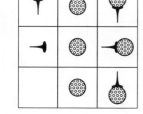

     a   **b**   **c**   **d**   **e**

8.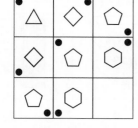

     a   **b**   **c**   **d**   **e**

121

Work out which option is the 3D figure viewed from the **right**.

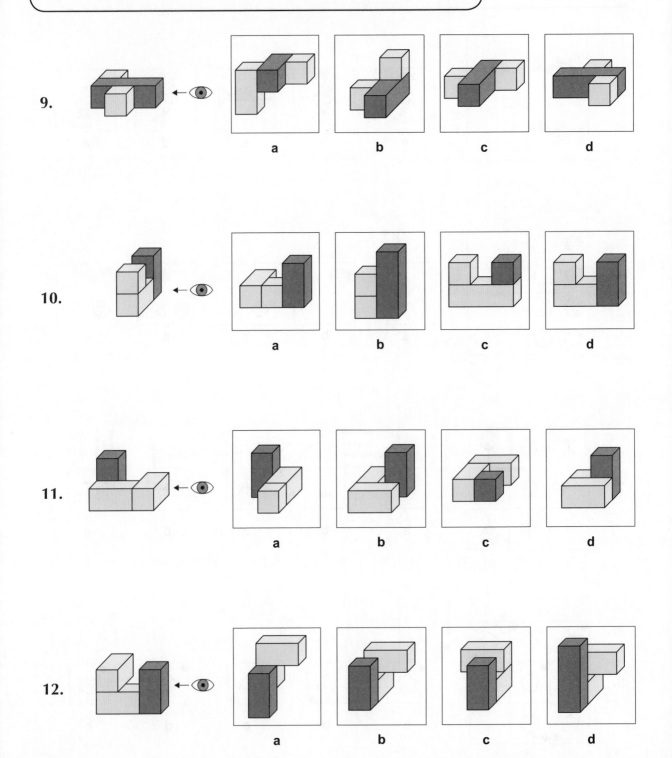

9.

a   b   c   d

10.

a   b   c   d

11.

a   b   c   d

12.

a   b   c   d

122

13.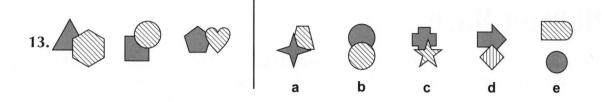

a   b   c   d   e

14.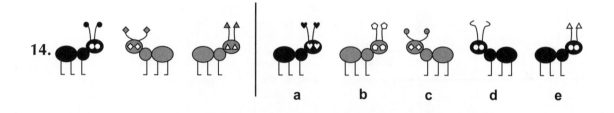

a   b   c   d   e

15.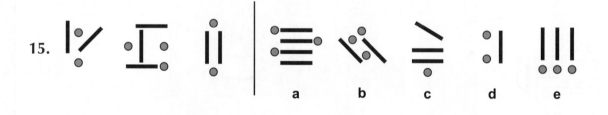

a   b   c   d   e

16.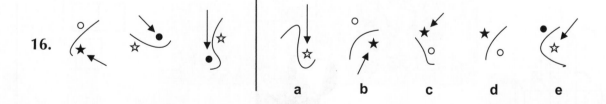

a   b   c   d   e

/ 16

Here's a puzzle which is great for practising your **2D** and **3D shape** skills.

Monster Maze

Greg is searching a cave for treasure which is guarded by monsters. He has five keys that will let him pass through doors in the cave. The bottom layer of cubes on the keys must exactly cover the grey squares on the grids to unlock the doors. Number each key from 1-5 in the order Greg will have to use them.

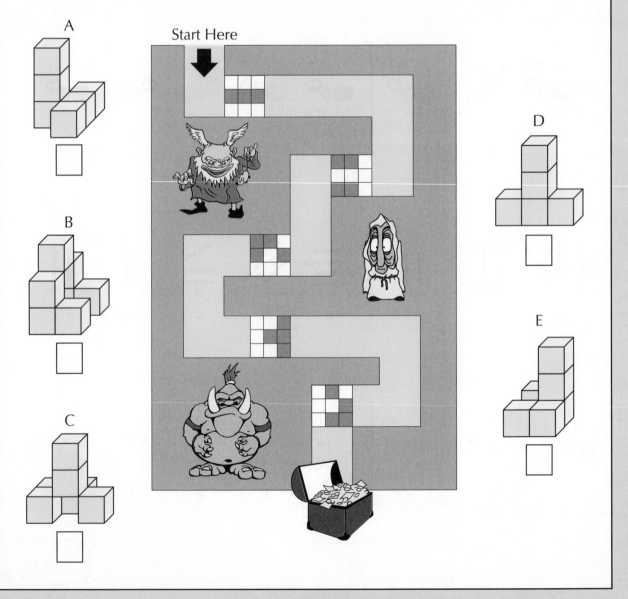

Test 28

You have **10 minutes** to do this test. Circle the letter for each correct answer.

Work out which option is the 3D figure viewed from the **right**.

1.

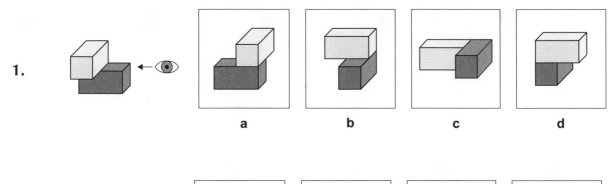

         a   b   c   d

2.

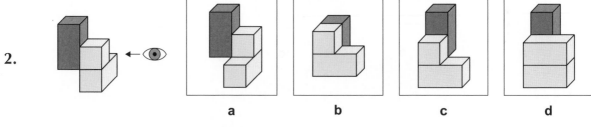

         a   b   c   d

3.

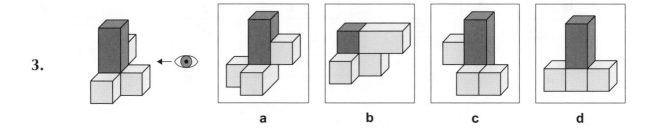

         a   b   c   d

4.

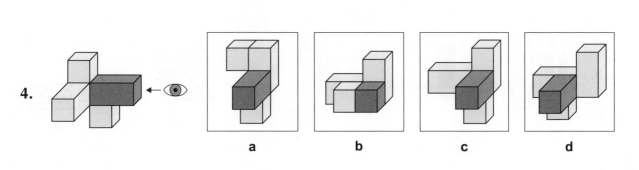

         a   b   c   d

                                125   Test 28

Find the figure in each row that is most unlike the others.

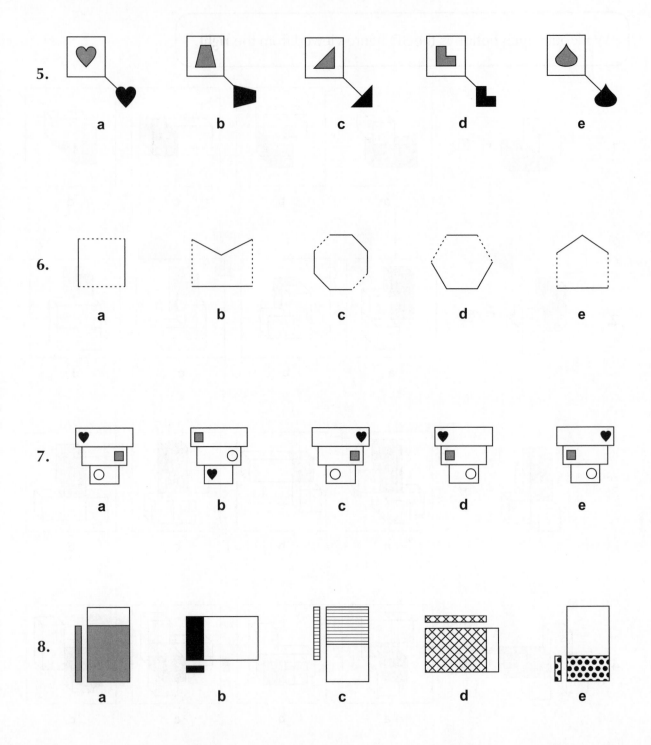

5. a   b   c   d   e

6. a   b   c   d   e

7. a   b   c   d   e

8. a   b   c   d   e

Work out which option is most like the three figures on the left.

9.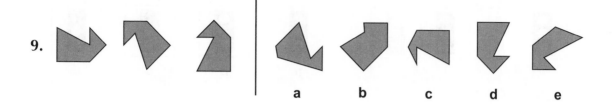

a   b   c   d   e

10.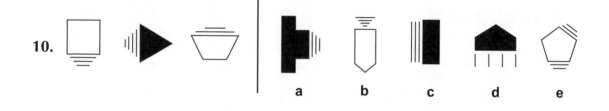

a   b   c   d   e

11.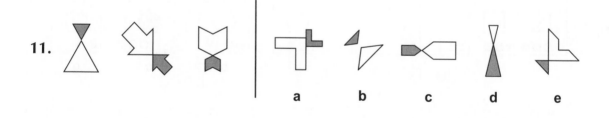

a   b   c   d   e

12.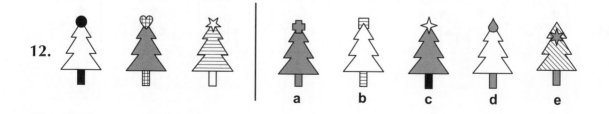

a   b   c   d   e

Test 28

Work out which of the options best fits in place of the missing square in the series.

13.

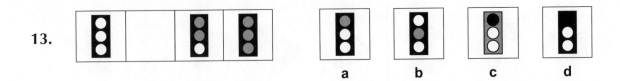

a   b   c   d

14.

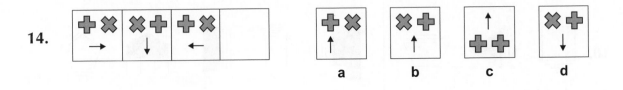

a   b   c   d

15.

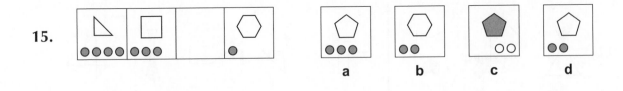

a   b   c   d

16.

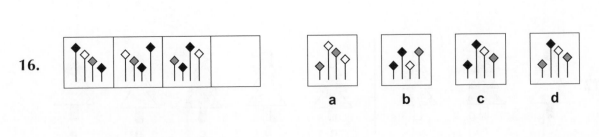

a   b   c   d

/ 16

Test 29

You have **10 minutes** to do this test. Circle the letter for each correct answer.

> Work out which option would look like the figure on the left if it was reflected over the line.

Reflect

1. | **a**   **b**   **c**   **d**

2. | **a**   **b**   **c**   **d**

Reflect

3. | **a** **b** **c** **d**

Reflect

4. | **a**   **b**   **c** **d**

© CGP — not to be photocopied

129

Test 29

Work out which option is most like the two figures on the left.

5.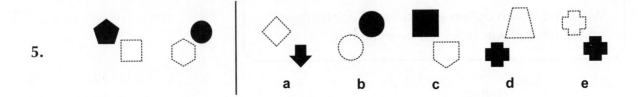

a b c d e

6.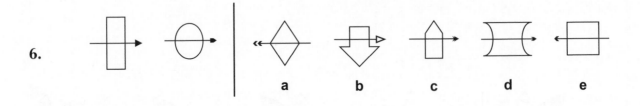

a b c d e

7.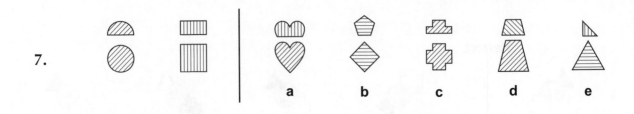

a b c d e

8.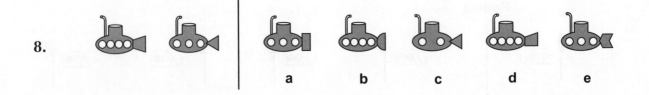

a b c d e

130

Work out which option is a top-down 2D view of the 3D figure on the left.

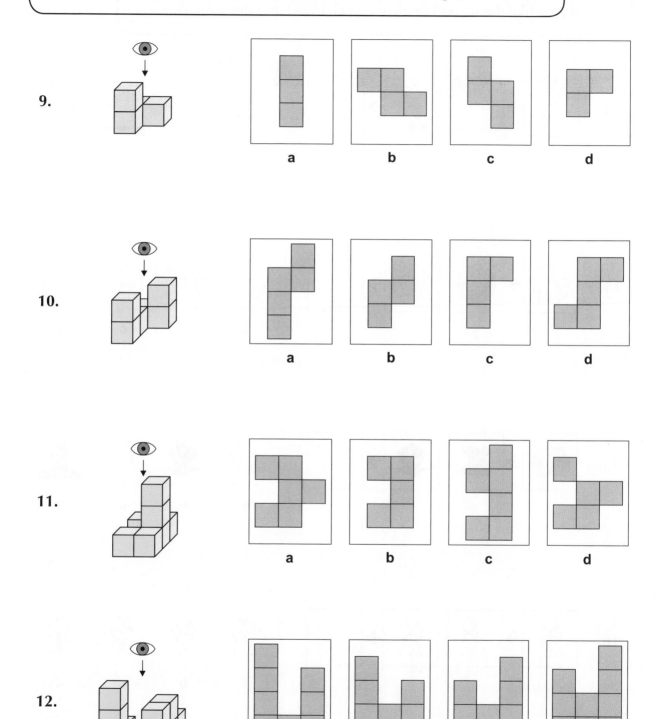

9.

a   b   c   d

10.

a   b   c   d

11.

a   b   c   d

12.

a   b   c   d

Test 29

Look at how the first figure is changed, and then work out which option would look like the second figure if you changed it in the same way.

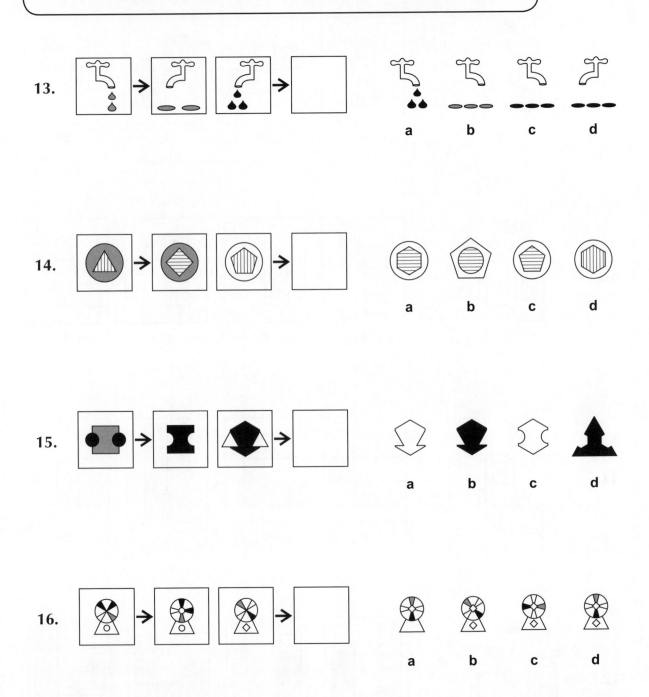

13.

a   b   c   d

14.

a   b   c   d

15.

a   b   c   d

16.

a   b   c   d

/ 16

132

You have **10 minutes** to do this test. Circle the letter for each correct answer.

Work out which option is most like the three figures on the left.

1.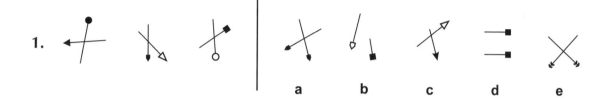

                                   a   **b**   **c**   **d**   **e**

2.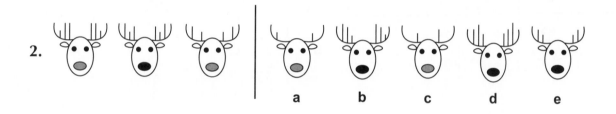

                                   a   **b**   **c**   **d**   **e**

3.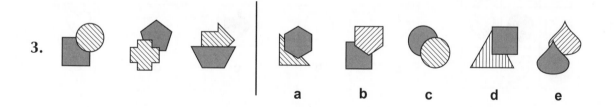

                                   a   **b**   **c**   **d**   **e**

4.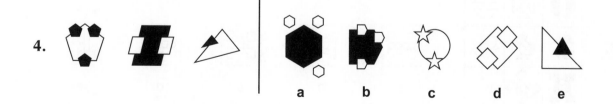

                                   a   **b**   **c**   **d**   **e**

                                      Test 30

Work out which of the options best fits in place of the missing square in the grid.

5.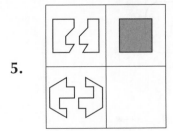

a b c d e

6.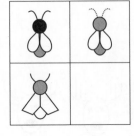

a b c d e

7.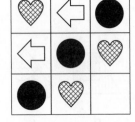

a b c d e

8.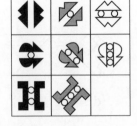

a b c d e

Find the figure in each row that is most unlike the others.

9.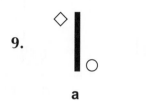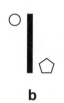

    a   **b**   **c**   **d**   **e**

10.

    a   **b**   **c**   **d**   **e**

11.

    a   **b**   **c**   **d**   **e**

12.

    a   **b**   **c**   **d**   **e**

135

Work out which option is the 3D figure viewed from the **right**.

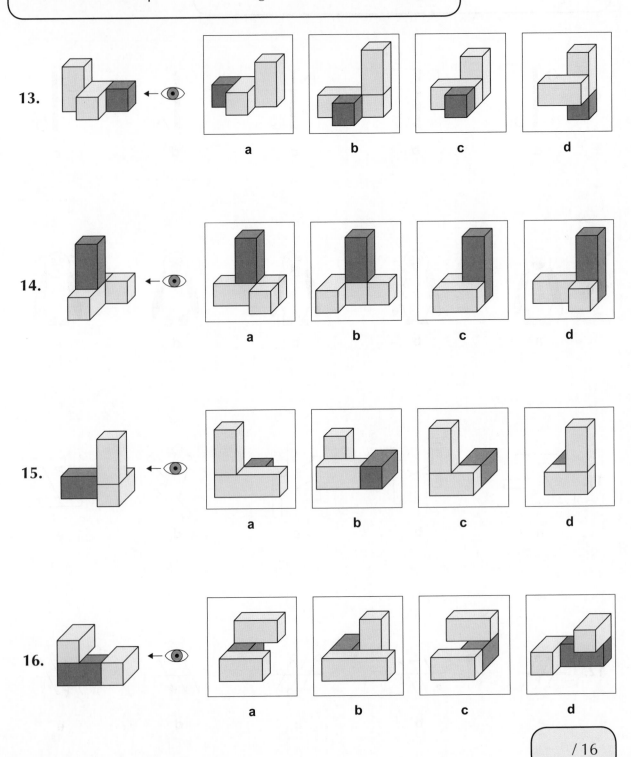

13. a b c d

14. a b c d

15. a b c d

16. a b c d

/ 16

You have **10 minutes** to do this test. Circle the letter for each correct answer.

Work out which option would look like the figure on the left if it was rotated.

1. **Rotate**

a
b
c
d

2. 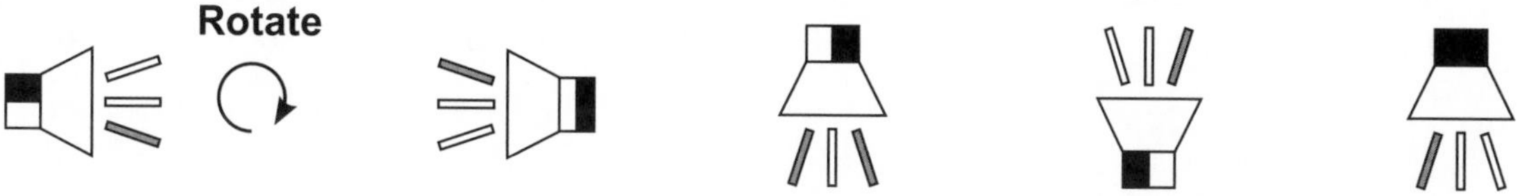 **Rotate**
a
b
c
d

3. 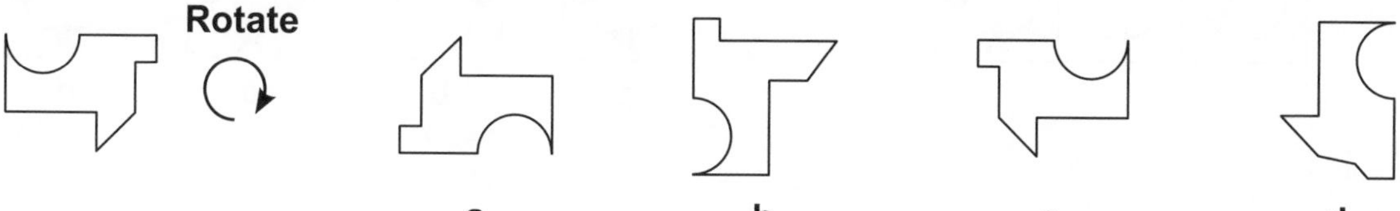 **Rotate**
a
b
c
d

4. 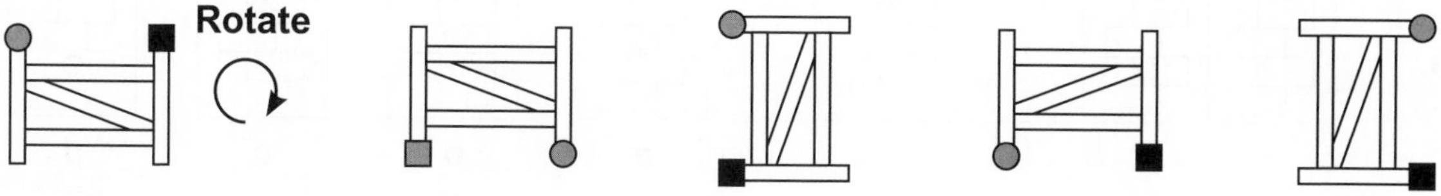 **Rotate**
a
b
c
d

137

5.

a   b   c   d

6.

7.

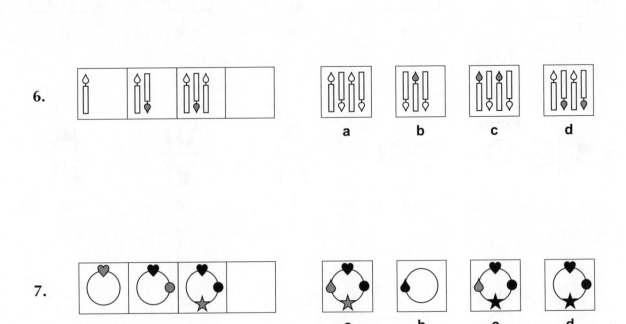

a   b   c   d

8.

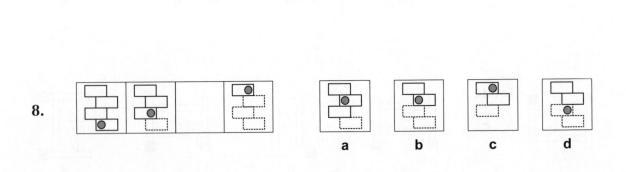

a   b   c   d

Work out which option is a top-down 2D view of the 3D figure on the left.

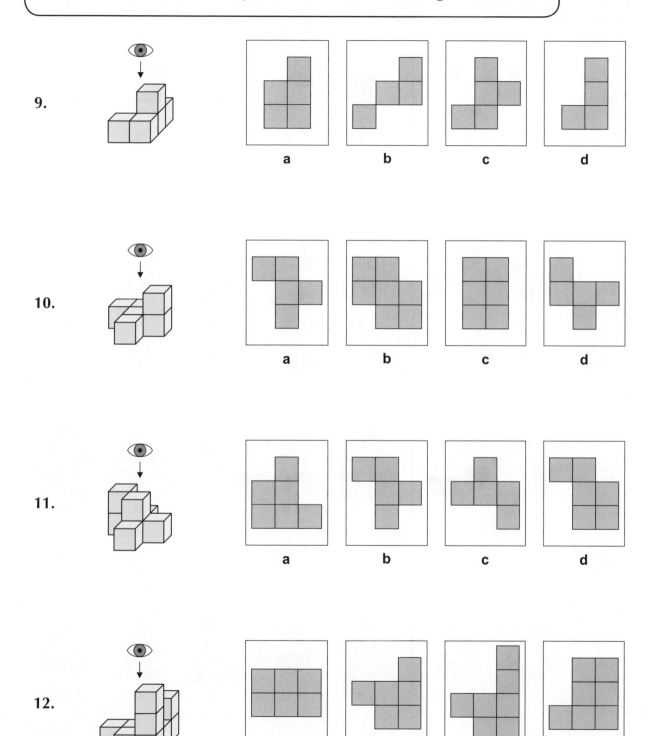

9.

a   b   c   d

10.

a   b   c   d

11.

a   b   c   d

12.

a   b   c   d

Test 31

Work out which option is most like the two figures on the left.

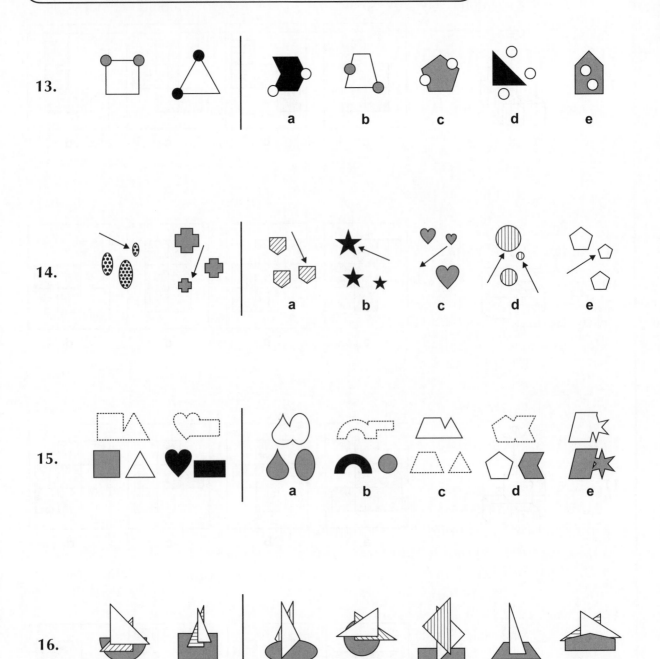

13. a b c d e

14. a b c d e

15. a b c d e

16. a b c d e

/ 16

That's the last test done. Here are some final puzzles to help you practise your skills.

Evolving Aliens

Aliens from the planet Zoog change into adults in five stages. Only one feature changes in each stage. Write the letters in the boxes to put the stages in order.

1.

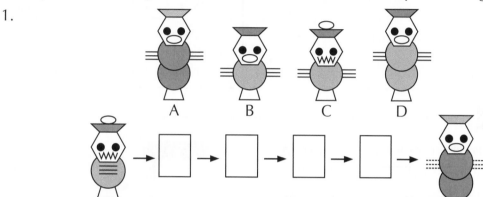

In the empty boxes below, draw what these aliens will look like as adults.

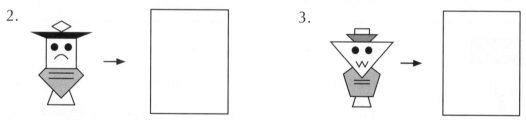

2.   3.

Monumental Success

King Zag of Zoog is building a monument in honour of himself. He has made a plan for the front of the monument, but is unsure what it will look like from the right-hand side. Circle the correct view of the monument from the right.

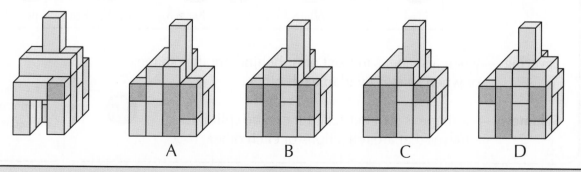

A   B   C   D

141

Glossary

Rotation

Rotation is when a shape is turned clockwise or anticlockwise.

Example
shape

45 degree
rotation

90 degree
rotation

180 degree
rotation

Clockwise is the
direction that the hands
on a clock move.

Anticlockwise is
the opposite
direction.

Reflection

Reflection is when something is mirrored
over a line (this line might be invisible).

The black shape is
reflected across to
make the white shape.

The black shape is
reflected down to
make the grey shape.

Other Terms

Figure — the picture as a whole that makes up one example or option in a question.

Line Types:

Thin   Thick   Dashed   Dotted   Curved   Jagged   Wavy

Shading Types:

Black   Grey   White   Two types of hatching   Cross-hatched   Spotted

Layering — when a shape is in front of or behind another shape,
or when shapes overlap each other.

The circle is
in front of
the square.

Symmetry — a shape is symmetrical if it can be split into
halves that are reflections of each other.

N4XPDE1